PEARSON

ALWAYS LEARNING

Scott Freeman • Lizabeth Allison • Michael Black
Greg Podgorski • Kim Quillin • Jon Monroe • Emily Taylor

Biological Science

Custom Edition for Emory University

Taken from:
Biological Science, Fifth Edition
by Scott Freeman, Lizabeth Allison, Michael Black,
Greg Podgorski, Kim Quillin, Jon Monroe, and Emily Taylor

Cover Art: Courtesy of Photodisc/Getty Images.

Taken from:

Biological Science, Fifth Edition
by Scott Freeman, Lizabeth Allison, Michael Black, Greg Podgorski, Kim Quillin, Jon Monroe, and Emily Taylor
Copyright © 2014, 2011, 2008 by Pearson Education, Inc.
Boston, Massachusetts 02116

This special edition published in cooperation with Pearson Learning Solutions.

All trademarks, service marks, registered trademarks, and registered service marks are the property of their respective owners and are used herein for identification purposes only.

Pearson Learning Solutions, 501 Boylston Street, Suite 900, Boston, MA 02116
A Pearson Education Company
www.pearsoned.com

Printed in the United States of America

1 2 3 4 5 6 7 8 9 10 VOCR 18 17 16 15 14

000200010271904897

PJ

PEARSON

ISBN 10: 1-269-93515-1
ISBN 13: 978-1-269-93515-9

Detailed Contents

25 Evolution by Natural Selection

In this chapter you will learn that

Evolution is one of the most important ideas in modern biology

by reviewing → The evolution of evolutionary thought **25.1**

by asking → What is the evidence for evolution?

by applying → Evolution in action: two case studies **25.4**

with regard to

The pattern of evolution: species have changed and are related **25.2**

The process of evolution by natural selection **25.3**

keeping in mind

Common misconceptions **25.5**

Natural selection acts on individuals in populations such as these sea stars, but only populations evolve. One of Darwin's greatest contributions to science was the introduction of population thinking to the theory of evolution.

This chapter is part of the Big Picture. See how on pages 526–527.

This chapter is about one of the great ideas in science. The theory of evolution by natural selection, formulated independently by Charles Darwin and Alfred Russel Wallace, explains how organisms have come to be adapted to environments ranging from arctic tundra to tropical wet forest. It revealed one of the five key attributes of life: Populations of organisms evolve—meaning that they change through time (Chapter 1).

As an example of a revolutionary breakthrough in our understanding of the world, the theory of evolution by natural selection ranks alongside Copernicus's theory of the Sun as the center of our solar system, Newton's laws of motion and theory of gravitation, the germ theory of disease, the theory of plate tectonics, and Einstein's general theory of relativity. These theories are the foundation stones of modern science; all are accepted on the basis of overwhelming evidence.

✔ When you see this checkmark, stop and test yourself. Answers are available in Appendix A.

Evolution by natural selection is one of the best supported and most important theories in the history of scientific research. But like most scientific breakthroughs, this one did not come easily. When Darwin published his theory in 1859 in a book called *On the Origin of Species by Means of Natural Selection*, it unleashed a firestorm of protest throughout Europe. At that time, the leading explanation for the diversity of organisms was an idea called special creation.

Special creation held that: **(1)** All species are independent, in the sense of being unrelated to each other; **(2)** life on Earth is young—perhaps just 6000 years old; and **(3)** species are immutable, or incapable of change. These beliefs were explained by the instantaneous and independent creation of living organisms by a supernatural being.

Darwin's theory was radically different. How did it differ? Scientific theories usually have two components: a pattern and a process (see Chapter 1):

1. The *pattern component* is a statement that summarizes a series of observations about the natural world. The pattern component is about facts—about how things *are* in nature.

2. The *process component* is a mechanism that produces that pattern or set of observations.

Let's begin with an overview of the evolution of evolutionary thought, and then examine the pattern and process components of the theory of evolution by natural selection.

25.1 The Evolution of Evolutionary Thought

People often use the word revolutionary to describe the theory of evolution by natural selection. Revolutions overturn things—they replace an existing entity with something new and often radically different. A political revolution removes the ruling class or group and replaces it with another. The industrial revolution replaced small shops for manufacturing goods by hand with huge, mechanized assembly lines.

A scientific revolution, in contrast, overturns an existing idea about how nature works and replaces it with another, radically different, idea. The idea that Darwin and Wallace overturned—that species were supernaturally, not naturally, created—had dominated thinking about the nature of organisms in Western civilization for over 2000 years.

Plato and Typological Thinking

The Greek philosopher Plato claimed that every organism was an example of a perfect essence, or type, created by God, and that these types were unchanging. Plato acknowledged that the individual organisms present on Earth might deviate slightly from the perfect type, but he said this deviation was similar to seeing the perfect type in a shadow on a wall. The key to understanding life, in Plato's mind, was to ignore the shadows and focus on understanding each type of unchanging, perfect essence.

Today, philosophers and biologists refer to ideas like this as typological thinking. Typological thinking is based on the idea that species are unchanging types and that variations within species are unimportant or even misleading. Typological thinking also occurs in the Bible's book of Genesis, where God creates each type of organism.

Aristotle and the Great Chain of Being

Not long after Plato developed his ideas, Aristotle ordered the types of organisms known at the time into a linear scheme called the great chain of being, also called the scale of nature (**FIGURE 25.1**). Aristotle proposed that species were organized into a sequence based on increased size and complexity, with humans at the top. He also claimed that the characteristics of species were fixed—they did not change through time.

In the 1700s Aristotle's ideas were still popular in scientific and religious circles. The central claims were that **(1)** species are fixed types, and **(2)** some species are higher—in the sense of being more complex or "better"—than others.

Lamarck and the Idea of Evolution as Change through Time

Typological thinking eventually began to break down. In 1809 the biologist Jean-Baptiste de Lamarck proposed a formal theory of **evolution**—that species are not static but change through time. However, the pattern component of Lamarck's theory was initially based on the great chain of being.

When he started his work on evolution, Lamarck claimed that simple organisms originate at the base of the chain by

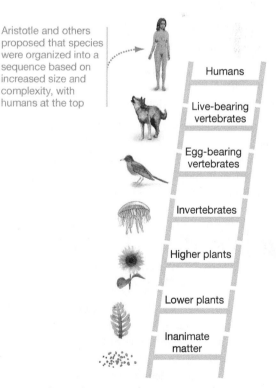

Aristotle and others proposed that species were organized into a sequence based on increased size and complexity, with humans at the top

Humans

Live-bearing vertebrates

Egg-bearing vertebrates

Invertebrates

Higher plants

Lower plants

Inanimate matter

FIGURE 25.1 The Great Chain of Being, or Scale of Nature.

spontaneous generation (see Chapter 1) and then evolve by moving up the chain over time. Thus, Lamarckian evolution is progressive in the sense of always producing larger and more complex, or "better," species. To capture this point, biologists often say that Lamarck turned the ladder of life into an escalator.

Lamarck also contended that species change through time via the inheritance of acquired characters. The idea here is that as an individual develops in response to challenges posed by the environment, its phenotype changes, and it passes on these phenotypic changes to offspring. A classic Lamarckian scenario is that giraffes develop long necks as they stretch to reach leaves high in treetops, and they then produce offspring with elongated necks.

Darwin and Wallace and Evolution by Natural Selection

As his thinking matured, Lamarck eventually abandoned his linear and progressive view of life. Darwin and Wallace concurred. But more important, they emphasized that the process responsible for change through time—evolution—occurs because traits vary among the individuals in a population, and because individuals with certain traits leave more offspring than others do. A **population** consists of individuals of the same species that are living in the same area at the same time.

Darwin and Wallace's proposal was a radical break from the typological thinking that had dominated scientific thought since Plato. Darwin claimed that instead of being unimportant or an illusion, variation among individuals in a population was the key to understanding the nature of species. Biologists refer to this view as **population thinking.**

The theory of evolution by natural selection was revolutionary for several reasons:

1. It overturned the idea that species are static and unchanging.

2. It replaced typological thinking with population thinking.

3. It was scientific. It proposed a mechanism that could account for change through time and made predictions that could be tested through observation and experimentation.

Plato and his followers emphasized the existence of fixed types; evolution by natural selection is all about change and diversity. Now the questions are: What evidence backs the claim that species are not fixed types? What data convince biologists that the theory of evolution by natural selection is correct?

25.2 The Pattern of Evolution: Have Species Changed, and Are They Related?

In *On the Origin of Species*, Darwin repeatedly described evolution as **descent with modification.** He meant that species that lived in the past are the ancestors of the species existing today, and that species change through time.

This view was a radical departure from the independently created and immutable species embodied in Plato's work and in the idea of special creation. In essence, the pattern component of the theory of evolution by natural selection makes two predictions about the nature of species:

1. Species change through time.

2. Species are related by common ancestry.

Let's consider the evidence for each of these predictions in turn.

Evidence for Change through Time

When Darwin began his work, biologists and geologists had just begun to assemble and interpret the fossil record. A **fossil** is any trace of an organism that lived in the past. These traces range from bones and branches to shells, tracks or impressions, and dung. The **fossil record** consists of all the fossils that have been found on Earth and described in the scientific literature.

Why did data in the fossil record support the hypothesis that species have changed through time? And what data from **extant species**—those living today—support the claim that they are modified forms of ancestral species?

The Vastness of Geologic Time Initially, fossils were organized according to their *relative* ages based on a series of principles derived from observations about rock formation. **Sedimentary rocks,** for example, form from sand or mud or other materials deposited at locations such as beaches or river mouths. Sedimentary rocks, along with rocks derived from volcanic ash or lava, are known to form in layers—younger layers are deposited on top of older layers.

Researchers used this information to place fossils in a younger-to-older sequence, based on the fossils' relative position in layers of sedimentary rock (**FIGURE 25.2**). As the scientists observed similarities in rocks and fossils at different sites, they began to create a **geologic time scale:** a sequence of named intervals called eons, eras, and periods that represented the major events in Earth history (see Chapter 28). They also realized that vast amounts of time were required to form the thick layers of sedimentary rock that they were studying, because erosion and deposition of sediments are such slow processes.

This was an important insight. The geologic record indicated that the Earth was much, much older than the 6000 years claimed by proponents of special creation.

After the discovery of radioactivity in the late 1800s, researchers realized that radioactive decay—the steady rate at which unstable or "parent" atoms are converted into more stable "daughter" atoms—furnished a way to assign *absolute* ages, in years, to the relative ages in the geologic time scale.

Radiometric dating is based on three pieces of information:

1. Observed decay rates of parent to daughter atoms

2. The ratio of parent to daughter atoms present in newly formed rocks—such as the amount of uranium atoms versus lead atoms when uranium-containing molten rock first cools (Uranium decays to form lead.)

3. The ratio of parent to daughter atoms present in a particular rock sample

Younger rock layers   **Younger fossils**

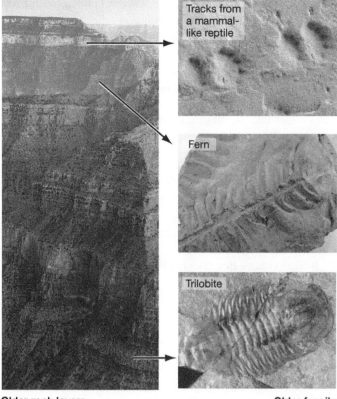

Tracks from a mammal-like reptile

Fern

Trilobite

Older rock layers   **Older fossils**

FIGURE 25.2 Sedimentary Rocks Reveal the Vastness of Geologic Time. The relative ages of sedimentary rocks are used to determine the relative ages of fossil organisms because younger layers are deposited on top of older ones. The deepest rock layer in the Grand Canyon is over a billion years old, and the top layer is 270 million years old.

Combining information from these two ratios with information on the decay rate allows researchers to estimate how long ago a rock formed. According to data from radiometric dating, Earth is about 4.6 billion years old, and the earliest signs of life appear in rocks that formed 3.4–3.8 billion years ago.

Data from relative and absolute dating techniques agree: Life on Earth is ancient. A great deal of time has gone by for change to occur.

Extinction Changes the Species Present over Time   In the early nineteenth century, researchers began discovering fossil bones, leaves, and shells that were unlike structures from any known animal or plant. At first, many scientists insisted that living examples of these species would be found in unexplored regions of the globe. But as research continued and the number and diversity of fossil collections grew, the argument became less and less plausible.

The issue was finally settled in 1812 when Baron Georges Cuvier published a detailed analysis of an **extinct species**—that is, a species that no longer exists—called the Irish "elk." Scientists accepted the fact of extinction because this gigantic deer was judged to be too large to have escaped discovery and too

FIGURE 25.3 Evidence of Extinction. The skeleton of the Irish "elk" dwarfs a human. Scientists agreed that the deer was too large and unique to be overlooked if it were alive; it must have gone extinct.

distinctive to be classified as a large-bodied population of an existing species (**FIGURE 25.3**).

Advocates of special creation argued that fossil species were victims of the flood at the time of Noah. Darwin, in contrast, interpreted extinct forms as evidence that species are not static, immutable entities, unchanged since the moment of special creation. His reasoning was that if species have gone extinct, then the array of species living on Earth has changed through time.

Recent analyses of the fossil record suggest that over 99 percent of all the species that have ever lived are now extinct. The data also indicate that species have gone extinct continuously throughout Earth's history—not just in one or even a few catastrophic events.

Transitional Features Link Older and Younger Species   Long before Darwin published his theory, researchers reported striking resemblances between the fossils found in the rocks underlying certain regions and the living species found in the same geographic areas. The pattern was so widespread that it became known as the "law of succession." The general observation was that extinct species in the fossil record were succeeded, in the same region, by similar species.

Early in the nineteenth century, the pattern was simply reported and not interpreted. But later, Darwin pointed out that it provided strong evidence in favor of the hypothesis that species had changed through time. His idea was that the extinct forms and living forms were related—that they represented ancestors and descendants.

As the fossil record expanded, researchers discovered species with characteristics that broadened the scope of the law of succession. A **transitional feature** is a trait in a fossil species that is intermediate between those of ancestral (older) and derived (younger) species. For example, intensive work over the past several decades has yielded fossils that document a gradual change over time from aquatic animals that had fins to terrestrial animals that had limbs (**FIGURE 25.4**). Over a period of about 25 million years, the fins of species similar to today's lungfish changed into limbs similar to those found in today's amphibians, reptiles, and mammals—a group called the tetrapods (literally, "four-footed").

These observations support the hypothesis that an ancestral lungfish-like species first used stout, lobed fins to navigate in shallow aquatic habitats. Then they moved onto land, where their descendants became more and more like today's tetrapods in appearance and lifestyle. Lungfish and tetrapod species have clearly changed through time.

Similar sequences of transitional features document changes that led to the evolution of feathers and flight in birds; stomata and vascular tissue in plants; upright posture, flattened faces, and large brains in humans; jaws in vertebrates (animals with backbones); the loss of limbs in snakes; and other traits. Data like these are consistent with predictions from the theory of evolution: If the traits observed in more recent species evolved from traits in more ancient species, then transitional forms are expected to occur in the appropriate time sequence.

The fossil record provides compelling evidence that species have evolved. What data from extant forms support the hypothesis that the characteristics of species change through time?

Vestigial Traits Are Evidence of Change through Time Darwin was the first to provide a widely accepted interpretation of vestigial traits. A **vestigial trait** is a reduced or incompletely developed structure that has no function, or reduced function, but is clearly similar to functioning organs or structures in closely related species.

Biologists have documented thousands of examples of vestigial traits.

- Some whales and snakes have tiny hip and leg bones that do not help them swim or slither.

- Ostriches and kiwis have reduced wings and cannot fly.

- Eyeless, blind cave-dwelling fish have eye sockets.

- Even though marsupial mammals give birth to live young, an eggshell forms briefly early in their development; in some species, newborns have a nonfunctioning "egg tooth" similar to those used by birds and reptiles to break open their shells.

- Monkeys and many other primates have long tails; but our coccyx, illustrated in **FIGURE 25.5**, is too small to help us maintain balance or grab tree limbs for support.

- Many mammals, including primates, are able to erect their hair when they are cold or excited. This behavior manifests itself as goose bumps in humans, but goose bumps are largely ineffective in warming us or signalling our emotional state.

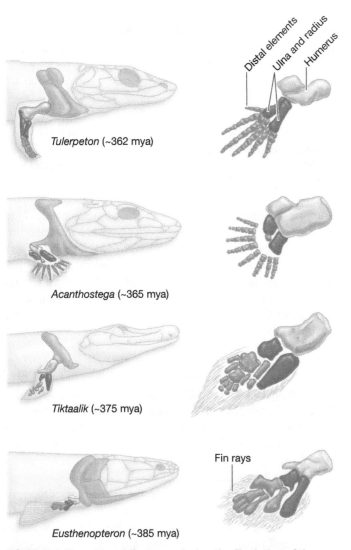

FIGURE 25.4 Transitional Features during the Evolution of the Tetrapod Limb. Fossil species similar to today's lungfish and tetrapods have fin and limb bones that are transitional features. *Eusthenopteron* was aquatic; *Tulerpeton* was probably semiaquatic (mya = million years ago).

✔**QUESTION** How would observations of transitional features be explained under special creation?

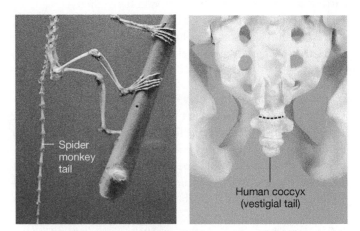

FIGURE 25.5 Vestigial Traits Are Reduced Versions of Traits in Other Species. The tailbone is a human trait that has reduced function. It is no longer useful for balance and locomotion.

✔**QUESTION** How would observations of vestigial traits be explained if evolution occurred via inheritance of acquired characters?

The existence of vestigial traits is inconsistent with the idea of special creation, which maintains that species were perfectly designed by a supernatural being and that the characteristics of species are static. Instead, vestigial traits are evidence that the characteristics of species have changed over time.

Current Examples of Change through Time Biologists have documented hundreds of contemporary populations that are changing in response to changes in their environment. Bacteria have evolved resistance to drugs; insects have evolved resistance to pesticides; weedy plants have evolved resistance to herbicides; the timing of bird migrations, the emergence of insects, and the blooming of flowering plants have evolved in response to climate change. Section 25.4 provides a detailed analysis of research on two examples of evolution in action.

To summarize, change through time continues and can be measured directly. Evidence from the fossil record and living species indicates that life is ancient, that species have changed through the course of Earth's history, and that species continue to change. The take-home message is that species are dynamic—not static, unchanging, and fixed types, as claimed by Plato, Aristotle, and advocates of special creation.

Evidence of Descent from a Common Ancestor

Data from the fossil record and contemporary species refute the hypothesis that species are immutable. What about the claim that species were created independently—meaning that they are unrelated to each other?

Similar Species Are Found in the Same Geographic Area Charles Darwin began to realize that species are related by common ancestry during a five-year voyage he took aboard the English naval ship HMS *Beagle*. While fulfilling its mission to explore and map the coast of South America, the *Beagle* spent a few weeks in the Galápagos Islands off the coast of present-day Ecuador. Darwin had taken over the role of ship's naturalist and, as the first scientist to study the area, gathered extensive collections of the plants and animals found in these islands. Most famous among the birds he collected were the Galápagos finches (featured in Section 25.4) and the Galápagos mockingbirds, pictured in **FIGURE 25.6a**.

Several years after Darwin returned to England, a colleague pointed out that the mockingbirds collected on different islands were distinct species, based on differences in coloration and beak size and shape. This struck Darwin as remarkable. Why would species that inhabit neighboring islands be so similar, yet clearly

(a) Pattern: Although the Galápagos mockingbirds are extremely similar, distinct species are found on different islands.

(b) Recent data support Darwin's hypothesis that the Galápagos mockingbirds share a common ancestor.

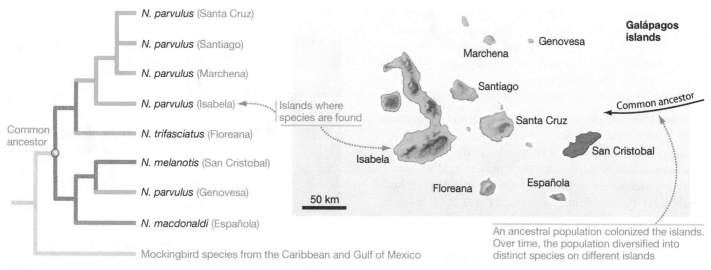

FIGURE 25.6 Close Relationships among Island Forms Argue for Shared Ancestry.

Gene:	Amino acid sequence (single-letter abbreviations):
Aniridia (Human)	LQRNRTSFTQEQIEALEKEFERTHYPDVFARERLAAKIDLPEARIQVWFSNRRAKWRREE
eyeless (Fruit fly)	LQRNRTSFTNDQIDSLEKEFERTHYPDVFARERLAGKIGLPEARIQVWFSNRRAKWRREE

FIGURE 25.7 Genetic Homology: Genes from Different Species May Be Similar in DNA Sequence or Other Attributes. Amino acid sequences from a portion of the *Aniridia* gene product found in humans are 90 percent identical to those found in the *Drosophila eyeless* gene product. (For a key to the single-letter abbreviations used for the amino acids, see Figure 3.2.)

distinct? This turns out to be a widespread pattern: In island groups across the globe, it is routine to find similar but distinct species on neighboring islands.

Darwin realized that this pattern—puzzling when examined as a product of special creation—made perfect sense when interpreted in the context of evolution, or descent with modification. The mockingbirds were similar, he proposed, because they had descended from the same common ancestor. That is, instead of being created independently, mockingbird populations that colonized different islands had changed through time and formed new species (**FIGURE 25.6b**).

Recent analyses of DNA sequences in these mockingbirds support Darwin's hypothesis. Researchers have used the DNA sequence comparisons to place the mockingbirds on a **phylogenetic tree**—a branching diagram that describes the ancestor–descendant relationships among species or other taxa (see Chapter 28). As Figure 25.6b shows, the Galápagos mockingbirds are each others' closest living relatives. As Darwin predicted, they share a single common ancestor. (For help with reading phylogenetic trees, see **BioSkills 7** in Appendix B.)

Similar Species Share Homologies Translated literally, homology means "the study of likeness." When biologists first began to study the anatomy of humans and other vertebrates, they were struck by the remarkable similarity of their skeletons, muscles, and organs. But because the biologists who did these early studies were advocates of special creation, they could not explain why striking similarities existed among certain organisms but not others.

Today, biologists recognize that **homology** is a similarity that exists in species because they inherited the trait from a common ancestor. Human hair and dog fur are homologous. Humans have hair and dogs have hair (fur) because they share a common ancestor—an early mammal species—that had hair.

Homology can be recognized and studied at three levels:

1. **Genetic homology** occurs in DNA nucleotide sequences, RNA nucleotide sequences, or amino acid sequences. For example, the *eyeless* gene in fruit flies and the *Aniridia* gene in humans are so similar that their protein products are 90 percent identical in amino acid sequence (**FIGURE 25.7**). Both genes act in determining where eyes will develop—even though fruit flies have a compound eye with many lenses and humans have a camera eye with a single lens.

2. **Developmental homology** is recognized in embryos. For example, early chick, human, and cat embryos have tails and

structures called gill pouches (**FIGURE 25.8**). Later, gill pouches are lost in all three species and tails are lost in humans. But in fish, the embryonic gill pouches stay intact and give rise to functioning gills in adults. To explain this observation, biologists hypothesize that gill pouches and tails exist in chicks, humans, and cats because they existed in the fishlike species that was the common ancestor of today's vertebrates. Embryonic gill pouches are a vestigial trait in chicks, humans, and cats; embryonic tails are a vestigial trait in humans.

3. **Structural homology** is a similarity in adult **morphology,** or form. A classic example is the common structural plan observed in the limbs of vertebrates (**FIGURE 25.9**). In Darwin's own words, "What could be more curious than that the hand of a man, formed for grasping, that of a mole for digging, the leg of the horse, the paddle of the porpoise, and the wing of the bat, should all be constructed on the same pattern, and should include the same bones, in the same relative positions?" An engineer would never use the same underlying structure to design a grasping tool, a digging implement, a walking device, a propeller, and a wing. Instead, the structural homology exists because mammals evolved from the lungfish-like ancestor in Figure 25.4, which had the same general arrangement of bones in its fins.

The three levels of homology interact. Genetic homologies cause the developmental homologies observed in embryos, which then lead to the structural homologies recognized in adults. Perhaps the most fundamental of all homologies is the genetic code.

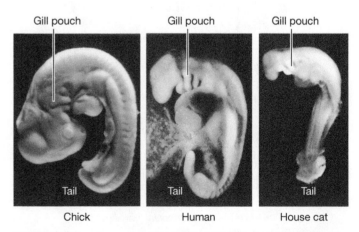

FIGURE 25.8 Developmental Homology: Structures That Appear Early in Development Are Similar. The early embryonic stages of a chick, a human, and a cat show a strong resemblance.

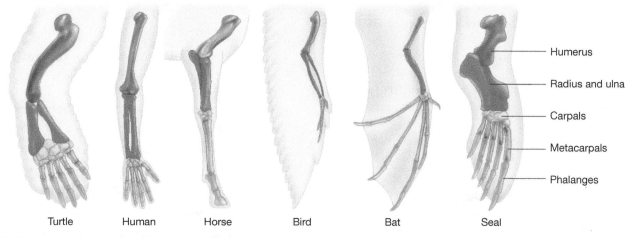

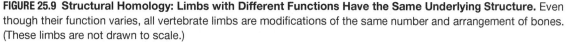

| Turtle | Human | Horse | Bird | Bat | Seal |

- Humerus
- Radius and ulna
- Carpals
- Metacarpals
- Phalanges

FIGURE 25.9 Structural Homology: Limbs with Different Functions Have the Same Underlying Structure. Even though their function varies, all vertebrate limbs are modifications of the same number and arrangement of bones. (These limbs are not drawn to scale.)

With a few minor exceptions, all organisms use the same rules for transferring the information coded in DNA into proteins (see Chapter 16).

In some cases, hypotheses about homology can be tested experimentally. For example, researchers (**1**) isolated a mouse gene that was thought to be homologous to the fruit fly *eyeless* gene, (**2**) inserted the mouse gene into fruit fly embryos, (**3**) stimulated expression of the foreign gene in locations that normally give rise to appendages, and (**4**) observed formation of eyes on legs and antennae (**FIGURE 25.10**). The function of the inserted gene was identical to that of *eyeless*. This result was strong evidence that the fruit fly and mouse genes are homologous, as predicted from their sequence similarity.

Homology is a key concept in contemporary biology:

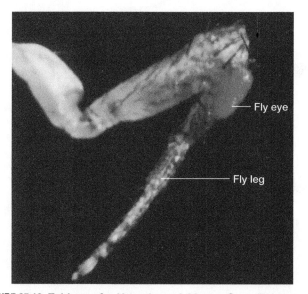

- Fly eye
- Fly leg

FIGURE 25.10 Evidence for Homology: A Mouse Gene Expressed in Fruit Flies. As an embryo, this fruit fly received a mouse gene that signals where eyes should form. A fruit fly eye formed in the location where the mouse gene was expressed.

- Chemicals that cause cancer in humans can often be identified by testing their effects on mutation rates in bacteria, yeast, zebrafish, mice, and other model organisms because the molecular machinery responsible for copying and repairing DNA is homologous in all organisms (see Chapter 15).

- Drugs intended for human use can be tested on mice or rabbits if the molecules targeted by the drugs are homologous.

- Unknown sequences in the human, rice, or other genomes can be identified if they are homologous to known sequences in yeast, fruit flies, or other well-studied model organisms (see Chapter 21 and **BioSkills 13** in Appendix B).

The theory of evolution by natural selection predicts that homologies will occur. If species were created independently of one another, as special creation claims, these types of similarities would not occur.

Current Examples of Descent from a Common Ancestor Biologists have documented dozens of contemporary populations that are undergoing speciation—a process that results in one species splitting into two or more descendant species. Some populations have served as particularly well-studied examples of speciation in action (see Chapter 27). In most cases, the identity of the ancestral species and the descendant species is known—meaning that biologists have established a direct link between ancestral and descendant species. In addition, the reason for the splitting event is usually known.

The contemporary examples of new species being formed are powerful evidence that species living today are the descendants of species that lived in the past. They support the claim that all organisms are related by descent from a common ancestor.

Evolution's "Internal Consistency"— The Importance of Independent Data Sets

Biologists draw upon data from several sources to challenge the hypothesis that species are immutable and were created independently. The data support the idea that species have descended, with modification, from a common ancestor. **TABLE 25.1** summarizes this evidence.

Perhaps the most powerful evidence for any scientific theory, including evolution by natural selection, is what scientists call internal consistency. This is the observation that data from independent sources agree in supporting predictions made by a theory.

As an example, consider the evolution of whales and dolphins—a group called the cetaceans.

- The fossil record contains a series of species that are clearly identified as cetaceans based on the unusual ear bones found only in this group. Some of the species have the long legs and compact bodies typical of mammals that live primarily on land; some are limbless and have the streamlined bodies typical of aquatic mammals; some have intermediate features.

- A phylogeny of the fossil cetaceans, estimated on the basis of similarities and differences in morphological traits other than limbs and overall body shape, indicates that a gradual transition occurred between terrestrial forms and aquatic, whale-like forms (**FIGURE 25.11**).

SUMMARY TABLE 25.1 **Evidence for Evolution**

Prediction 1: Species Are Not Static, but Change through Time

- Life on Earth is ancient. Most species have gone extinct.
- Fossil (extinct) species frequently resemble living species found in the same area.
- Transitional features document change in traits through time.
- Vestigial traits are common.
- The characteristics of populations vary within species and can be observed changing today.

Prediction 2: Species Are Related, Not Independent

- Closely related species often live in the same geographic area.
- Homologous traits are common and are recognized at three levels:
  1. genetic (gene structure and the genetic code)
  2. developmental (embryonic structures and processes)
  3. structural (morphological traits in adults)
- The formation of new species, from preexisting species, can be observed today.

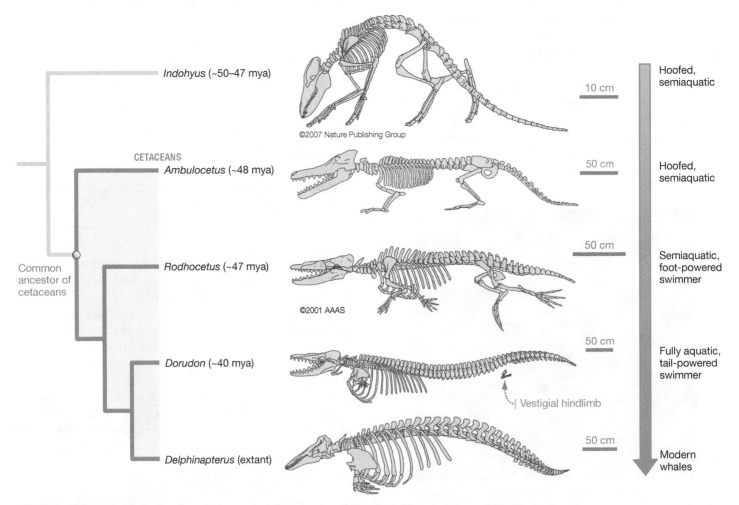

FIGURE 25.11 Data on Evolution from Independent Sources Are Consistent. This phylogeny of fossil cetaceans is consistent with data from relative dating, absolute dating, and phylogenies estimated from molecular traits in living species—all agree that whales evolved from terrestrial ancestors that were related to today's hippos.

- Relative dating, based on the positions of sedimentary rocks where the fossils were found, agrees with the order of species indicated in the phylogeny.

- Absolute dating, based on analyses of radioactive atoms in rocks in or near the layers where the fossils were found, also agrees with the order of species indicated in the phylogeny.

- A phylogeny of living whales and dolphins, estimated from similarities and differences in DNA sequences, indicates that hippos—which spend much of their time in shallow water—are the closest living relative of cetaceans. This observation supports the hypothesis that cetaceans and hippos shared a common ancestor that was semiaquatic.

- Some whales have vestigial hip and limb bones as adults, and some dolphin embryos have vestigial hindlimb buds—outgrowths where legs form in other mammals.

The general message here is that many independent lines of evidence converge on the same conclusion: Whales gradually evolved from a terrestrial ancestor about 50 million years ago.

As you evaluate the evidence supporting the pattern component of the theory of evolution, though, it's important to recognize that no single observation or experiment instantly "proved" the fact of evolution and swept aside belief in special creation. Rather, data from many different sources are much more consistent with evolution than with special creation. Descent with modification is a successful and powerful scientific theory because it explains observations—such as vestigial traits and the close relationships among species on neighboring islands—that special creation does not.

What about the process component of the theory of evolution by natural selection? If the limbs of bats and humans were not created independently and recently, how did they come to be?

25.3 The Process of Evolution: How Does Natural Selection Work?

Darwin's greatest contribution did not lie in recognizing the fact of evolution. Lamarck and other researchers had proposed evolution long before Darwin began his work. Instead, Darwin's crucial insight lay in recognizing a process, called natural selection, that could explain the pattern of descent with modification.

Darwin's Inspiration

How did Darwin arrive at his insight? In part, he turned to pigeon breeding—a model system that would be easier to study and manipulate than populations in the wild. Pigeon breeding was popular in England at the time, offering a wealth of experience for Darwin to tap into. Also, pigeons could be maintained easily, and in Darwin's words, "the diversity of the breeds is something astonishing" (see examples in **FIGURE 25.12**).

Darwin crossbred pigeons and observed how characteristics were passed on to offspring. He could choose certain individuals with desirable traits to reproduce, thus manipulating the composition of the population by a process called **artificial selection**. It was clear to Darwin and other breeders that the diverse varieties were all descended from the wild rock pigeons.

Another influence on Darwin was the fortuitous publication of a book by Thomas Robert Malthus, *An Essay on the Principle of Population*, which inspired a great deal of discussion in England at the time. Malthus's studies of human populations in England and elsewhere led him to a startling conclusion: Since many more individuals are born than can survive, a "struggle for existence" occurs as people compete for food and places to live.

Darwin combined his observations of artificial selection with this notion of "struggle for existence" in natural populations, which he knew—from his extensive studies—contained variation. From this synthesis arose his concept of natural selection. Although both Darwin and Wallace arrived at the same idea, Darwin's name is more closely associated with the concept of natural selection because he thought of it first and provided extensive evidence for it in *On the Origin of Species*.

FIGURE 25.12 Diversity of Pigeon Breeds in Captivity. Darwin used the breeding of pigeons as a model system to study how the characteristics of populations can change over time.

Darwin's Four Postulates

Darwin broke the process of evolution by natural selection into four simple postulates (criteria) that form a logical sequence:

1. The individual organisms that make up a population vary in the traits they possess, such as their size and shape.

2. Some of the trait differences are heritable, meaning that they are passed on to offspring. For example, tall parents tend to have tall offspring.

3. In each generation, many more offspring are produced than can possibly survive. Thus, only some individuals in the population survive long enough to produce offspring, and among the individuals that produce offspring, some will produce more than others.

4. The subset of individuals that survive best and produce the most offspring is not a random sample of the population. Instead, individuals with certain heritable traits are more likely to survive and reproduce. **Natural selection** occurs when individuals with certain characteristics produce more offspring than do individuals without those characteristics. The individuals are selected naturally—meaning, by the environment.

Because the selected traits are passed on to offspring, the frequency of the selected traits increases from one generation to the next. We now know that traits are determined by alleles, particular versions of genes (see Chapter 14). Thus, the outcome of evolution by natural selection is a change in allele frequencies in a population over time.

In studying these criteria, you should realize that variation among individuals in a population is essential if evolution is to occur. Darwin had to introduce population thinking into biology because it is populations that change over time. To come up with these postulates and understand their consequences, Darwin had to think in a revolutionary way.

Today, biologists usually condense Darwin's four postulates into a two-part statement that communicates the essence of evolution by natural selection more forcefully: Evolution by natural selection occurs when (1) heritable variation leads to (2) differential reproductive success.

The Biological Definitions of Fitness, Adaptation, and Selection

To explain the process of natural selection, Darwin referred to successful individuals as "more fit" than other individuals. In doing so, he gave the word fitness a definition different from its everyday English usage. Biological **fitness** is the ability of an individual to produce surviving, fertile offspring relative to that ability in other individuals in the population.

Note that fitness is a measurable quantity. When researchers study a population in the lab or in the field, they can estimate the relative fitness of individuals by counting the number of surviving offspring each individual produces and comparing the data.

The concept of fitness, in turn, provides a compact way of formally defining adaptation. The biological meaning of adaptation,

like the biological meaning of fitness, is different from its normal English usage. In biology, an **adaptation** is a heritable trait that increases the fitness of an individual in a particular environment relative to individuals lacking the trait. Adaptations increase fitness—the ability to produce viable, fertile offspring. You can see the Big Picture of how adaptation and fitness relate to natural selection on pages 526–527.

Lastly, the term selection has a commonsense meaning in the context of artificial selection. Breeders *choose* which characteristics they want to keep or get rid of in their plant and animal breeds. However, the term selection has a very different meaning in the biological context of natural selection. Here, it refers to a passive process—differential reproduction as a result of heritable variation—not a purposeful choice.

25.4 Evolution in Action: Recent Research on Natural Selection

The theory of evolution by natural selection is testable. If the theory is correct, biologists should be able to test the validity of each of Darwin's postulates—documenting heritable variation and differential reproductive success in a wide array of natural populations.

This section summarizes two examples in which evolution by natural selection is being observed in nature. Literally hundreds of other case studies are available, involving a wide variety of traits and organisms. To begin, let's explore the evolution of drug resistance, one of the great challenges facing today's biomedical researchers and physicians.

Case Study 1: How Did *Mycobacterium tuberculosis* Become Resistant to Antibiotics?

Mycobacterium tuberculosis, the bacterium that causes **tuberculosis,** or TB, has long been a scourge of humankind. It usually infects the lungs and causes fever, coughing, sweats, weight loss, and often death. In Europe and the United States, TB was once as great a public health issue as cancer is now. It receded in importance during the early 1900s, though, for two reasons:

1. Advances in nutrition made people better able to fight off most *M. tuberculosis* infections quickly.

2. The development of antibiotics allowed physicians to stop even advanced infections.

In the late 1980s, however, rates of *M. tuberculosis* infection surged in many countries, and in 1993 the World Health Organization declared TB a global health emergency. Physicians were particularly alarmed because the strains of *M. tuberculosis* responsible for the increase were largely or completely resistant to antibiotics that were once extremely effective.

How and why did the evolution of drug resistance occur? The case of a single patient—a young man who lived in Baltimore—illustrates what is happening all over the world.

A Patient History The story begins when the individual was admitted to the hospital with fever and coughing. Chest X-rays, followed by bacterial cultures of fluid coughed up from the lungs, showed that he had an active TB infection. He was given several antibiotics for 6 weeks, followed by twice-weekly doses of the antibiotic rifampin for an additional 33 weeks. Ten months after therapy started, bacterial cultures from the patient's chest fluid indicated no *M. tuberculosis* cells. His chest X-rays were also normal. The antibiotics seemed to have cleared the infection.

Just two months after the TB tests proved normal, however, the young man was readmitted to the hospital with a fever, severe cough, and labored breathing. Despite being treated with a variety of antibiotics, including rifampin, he died of respiratory failure 10 days later. Samples of material from his lungs showed that *M. tuberculosis* was again growing actively there. But this time the bacterial cells were completely resistant to rifampin.

Drug-resistant *M. tuberculosis* cells had killed this patient. Where did they come from? Could a strain that was resistant to antibiotic treatment have evolved *within* him? To answer this question, a research team analyzed DNA from the drug-resistant strain and compared it with stored DNA from *M. tuberculosis* cells that had been isolated a year earlier from the same patient. After examining extensive stretches from each genome, the biologists were able to find only one difference: a point mutation in a gene called *rpoB*.

A Mutation in a Bacterial Gene Confers Resistance The *rpoB* gene codes for a component of RNA polymerase. This enzyme transcribes DNA to mRNA, so it is essential to the survival and reproduction of bacterial cells (see Chapter 17). In this case, the point mutation in the *rpoB* gene changed a cytosine to a thymine, forming a new allele for the *rpoB* gene (see Chapter 16). This missense mutation caused a change in the amino acid sequence of the RNA polymerase (from a serine to a leucine at the 153rd amino acid)—and a change in its shape.

This shape change proved critical. Rifampin, the antibiotic that was being used to treat the patient, works by binding to the RNA polymerase of *M. tuberculosis* and interfering with transcription. Bacterial cells with the C → T mutation continue to produce offspring efficiently even in the presence of the drug because the drug cannot bind efficiently to the mutant RNA polymerase.

These results suggest the steps that led to this patient's death (**FIGURE 25.13**).

1. By chance, one or a few of the bacterial cells present in the patient, before drug therapy started, happened to have the *rpoB* allele with the C → T mutation. Under normal conditions, mutant forms of RNA polymerase do not work as well as the more common form, so cells with the C → T mutation would not produce many offspring and would stay at low frequency—even while the overall population grew to the point of inducing symptoms that sent the young man to the hospital.

2. Therapy with rifampin began. In response, cells in the population with normal RNA polymerase began to grow much more slowly or to die outright. As a result, the overall bacterial population declined in size so drastically that the patient appeared to be cured—his symptoms began to disappear.

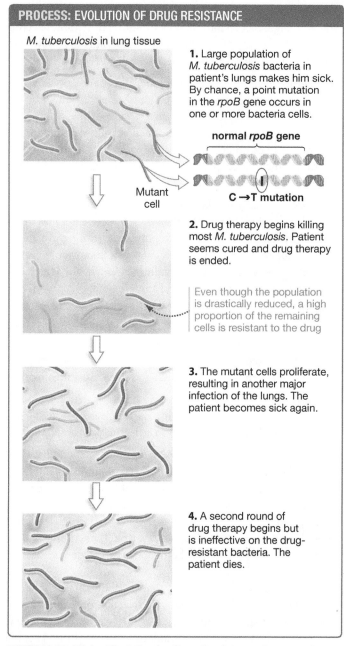

M. tuberculosis in lung tissue

1. Large population of *M. tuberculosis* bacteria in patient's lungs makes him sick. By chance, a point mutation in the *rpoB* gene occurs in one or more bacteria cells.

normal *rpoB* gene

Mutant cell

C → T mutation

2. Drug therapy begins killing most *M. tuberculosis*. Patient seems cured and drug therapy is ended.

Even though the population is drastically reduced, a high proportion of the remaining cells is resistant to the drug

3. The mutant cells proliferate, resulting in another major infection of the lungs. The patient becomes sick again.

4. A second round of drug therapy begins but is ineffective on the drug-resistant bacteria. The patient dies.

FIGURE 25.13 Alleles That Confer Drug Resistance Increase in Frequency When Drugs Are Used.

3. Cells with the C → T mutation continued to increase in number after therapy ended. Eventually the *M. tuberculosis* population regained its former abundance, and the patient's symptoms reappeared.

4. Drug-resistant *M. tuberculosis* cells now dominated the population, so the second round of rifampin therapy was futile.

✔ If you understand these concepts, you should be able to explain: (1) Why the relapse in step 3 occurred, and (2) whether a family member or health-care worker who got TB from this patient at step 3 or step 4 would respond to drug therapy.

Testing Darwin's Postulates Does the sequence of events illustrated in Figure 25.13 indicate that evolution by natural selection occurred? One way of answering this question is to review Darwin's four postulates and test whether each one was verified:

1. ***Did variation exist in the population?*** The answer is yes. Due to mutation, both resistant and nonresistant strains of TB were present before administration of the drug. Most *M. tuberculosis* populations, in fact, exhibit variation for the trait; studies on cultured *M. tuberculosis* show that a mutation conferring resistance to rifampin is present in one out of every 10^7 to 10^8 cells.

2. ***Was this variation heritable?*** The answer is yes. The researchers showed that the variation in the phenotypes of the two strains—from drug susceptibility to drug resistance—was due to variation in their genotypes. Because the mutant *rpoB* gene is passed on to daughter cells when a *Mycobacterium* replicates, the allele and the phenotype it produces—drug resistance—are passed on to offspring.

3. ***Was there variation in reproductive success?*** The answer is yes. Only a tiny fraction of *M. tuberculosis* cells in the patient survived the first round of antibiotics long enough to reproduce. Most cells died and left no or almost no offspring.

4. ***Did selection occur?*** The answer is yes. When rifampin was present, certain cells—those with the drug-resistant allele—had higher reproductive success than cells with the normal allele.

M. tuberculosis individuals with the mutant *rpoB* allele had higher fitness in an environment where rifampin was present. The mutant allele produces a protein that is an adaptation when the cell's environment contains the antibiotic.

This study verified all four postulates and confirmed that evolution by natural selection had occurred. The *M. tuberculosis* population evolved because the mutant *rpoB* allele increased in frequency.

It is critical to note, however, that the individual cells themselves did not evolve. When natural selection occurred, the individual bacterial cells did not change through time; they simply survived or died, or produced more or fewer offspring. This is a fundamentally important point: Natural selection acts on individuals, because individuals experience differential reproductive success. But only populations evolve. Allele frequencies change in populations, not in individuals. Understanding evolution by natural selection requires population thinking.

Drug Resistance: A Widespread Problem The events reviewed for this single patient have occurred many times in other patients. Recent surveys indicate that drug-resistant strains now account for about 10 percent of the *M. tuberculosis*–causing infections throughout the world.

Unfortunately, the emergence of drug resistance in TB is far from unusual. Resistance to a wide variety of insecticides, fungicides, antibiotics, antiviral drugs, and herbicides has evolved in hundreds of insects, fungi, bacteria, viruses, and plants. In every case, evolution has occurred because individuals with the

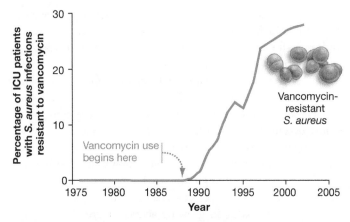

FIGURE 25.14 Trends in Infections Due to Antibiotic-resistant Bacteria. The line indicates changes in the percentage of *S. aureus* infections, acquired in hospitals, that are resistant to the antibiotic vancomycin.

DATA: Centers for Disease Control, 2004.

heritable ability to resist some chemical compound were present in the original population. As the susceptible individuals die from the pesticide, herbicide, or drug, the alleles that confer resistance increase in frequency.

To drive home the prevalence of evolution in response to drugs and other human-induced changes in the environment, consider the data in **FIGURE 25.14**. The graph shows changes through time in the percentage of infections, in intensive care units in the United States, caused by strains of the bacterium *Staphylococcus aureus* that are resistant to the antibiotic vancomycin. Most of these *S. aureus* cells are also resistant to methicillin and other antibiotics—a phenomenon known as multidrug resistance. In some cases, physicians have no effective antibiotics available to treat these infections. ✔ If you understand antibiotic resistance, you should be able to explain why the overprescription of antibiotics by doctors, or the overuse of everyday soaps and cleaners laced with antibiotics, can be a health risk.

Case Study 2: Why Are Beak Size, Beak Shape, and Body Size Changing in Galápagos Finches?

Can biologists study evolution in response to natural environmental change—when humans are not involved? The answer is yes. As an example, consider research led by Peter and Rosemary Grant. For over four decades, these biologists have been investigating changes in beak size, beak shape, and body size that have occurred in finches native to the Galápagos Islands.

Because the island of Daphne Major of the Galápagos is so small—about the size of 80 football fields—the Grants' team has been able to catch, weigh, and measure all the medium ground finches in the island's population (**FIGURE 25.15**) and mark each one with a unique combination of colored leg bands. The medium ground finch makes its living by eating seeds. Finches crack seeds with their beaks.

Early studies of the finch population established that beak size and shape and body size vary among individuals, and that beak

Medium ground finch
(*Geospiza fortis*)

Daphne Major

FIGURE 25.15 Studying Evolution in Action on the Galápagos.

FIGURE 25.16 A Natural Experiment: Changes in a Medium Ground Finch Population in Response to a Change in the Environment (a Drought). The results show the distribution of beak depth in the population of medium ground finches on Daphne Major before and after the drought of 1977. *N* is the population size.

SOURCE: Boag, P. T., and P. R. Grant. 1981. Intense natural selection in a population of Darwin's finches (Geospizinae) in the Galápagos. *Science* 214: 82–85.

✔**EXERCISE** Fill in the predictions made by the two hypotheses.

morphology and body size are heritable. Stated another way, parents with particularly deep beaks tend to have offspring with deep beaks. Large parents also tend to have large offspring. Beak size and shape and body size are traits with heritable variation.

Selection during Drought Conditions   Not long after the team began to study the finch population, a dramatic selection event occurred. In the annual wet season of 1977, Daphne Major received just 24 millimeters (mm) of rain instead of the 130 mm that normally falls. During the drought, few plants were able to produce seeds, and 84 percent (about 660 individuals) of the medium ground finch population disappeared.

Two observations support the hypothesis that most or all of these individuals died of starvation:

1. The researchers found 38 dead birds, and all were emaciated.

2. None of the missing individuals were spotted on nearby islands, and none reappeared once the drought had ended and food supplies returned to normal.

The research team realized that the die-off was a **natural experiment.** Instead of comparing groups created by direct manipulation under controlled conditions, natural experiments allow researchers to compare treatment groups created by an unplanned change in conditions. In this case, the Grants' team could test whether natural selection occurred by comparing the population before and after the drought.

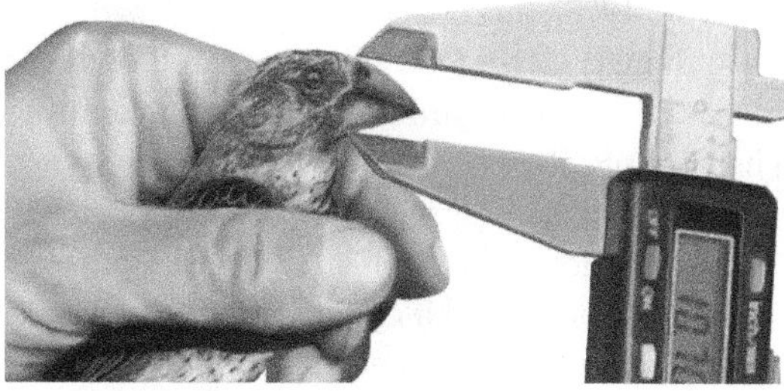

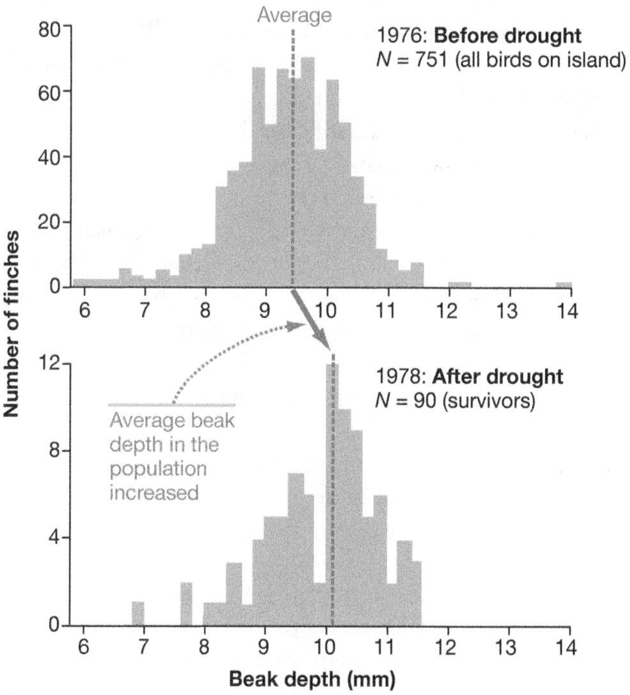

Were the survivors different from nonsurvivors? The histograms in **FIGURE 25.16** show the distribution of beak sizes in the population before and after the drought. Notice the different scales of the *y*-axes of the two graphs. (For more on how histograms are constructed, see **BioSkills 3** in Appendix B.) On average, survivors tended to have much deeper beaks than did the birds that died.

Why were deeper beaks adaptive? At the peak of the drought, most seed sources were absent and the tough fruits of a plant called *Tribulus cistoides* served as the finches' primary food source. These fruits are so difficult to crack that finches ignore them in years when food supplies are normal. The Grants hypothesized that individuals with particularly large and deep beaks were more likely to crack these fruits efficiently enough to survive.

At this point, the Grants had shown that natural selection led to an increase in average beak depth in the population. When breeding resumed in 1978, the offspring produced had beaks that were half a millimeter deeper, on average, than those in the population that existed before the drought. This result confirmed that evolution had occurred.

In only one generation, natural selection led to a measurable change in the characteristics of the population. Alleles that led to the development of deep beaks had increased in frequency in the population. Large, deep beaks were an adaptation for cracking large fruits and seeds.

Continued Changes in the Environment, Continued Selection, Continued Evolution In 1983, the environment on the Galápagos Islands changed again. Over a seven-month period, a total of 1359 mm of rain fell. Plant growth was luxuriant, and finches fed primarily on the small, soft seeds that were being produced in abundance. During this interval, small individuals with small, pointed beaks had exceptionally high reproductive success—meaning that they had higher fitness than those with large, deep beaks—because they were better able to harvest the small seeds. As a result, the characteristics of the population changed again. Alleles associated with small, pointed beaks increased in frequency.

Over subsequent decades, the Grants have documented continued evolution in response to continued changes in the environment. **FIGURE 25.17** documents changes that have occurred in average body size, beak size, and beak shape over 35 years. From 1972 to 2006, average body size got smaller and average beak size initially increased and then declined. In addition, finch beaks got much pointier.

Long-term studies like this are proving to be powerful because they have succeeded in documenting natural selection in response to changes in the environment.

Which Genes Are under Selection? Characteristics like body size, beak size, and beak shape are polygenic, meaning that many genes—each one exerting a relatively small effect—influence the trait (see Chapter 14). Because many genes are involved, it can be difficult for researchers to know exactly which alleles are changing in frequency when polygenic traits evolve.

To explore which of the medium ground finch's genes might be under selection, researchers in Clifford Tabin's lab began studying beak development in an array of Galápagos finch species. More specifically, they looked for variation in the pattern of expression of cell–cell signals that had already been identified as important in the development of chicken beaks. The hope was that homologous genes might affect beak development in finches.

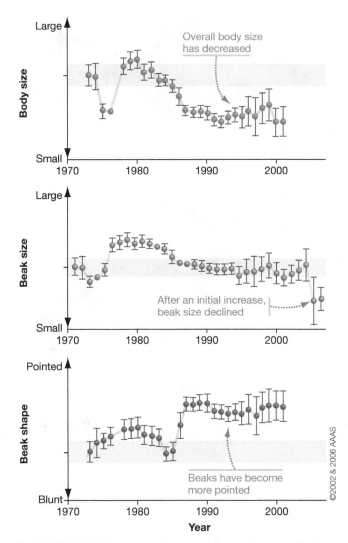

FIGURE 25.17 Body Size, Beak Size, and Beak Shape in Finches Changed over a 35-Year Interval.

DATA: Grant, P. R., and B. R. Grant. 2002. *Science* 296: 707–711; Grant, P. R., and B. R. Grant. 2006. *Science* 313: 224–226.

©2002 & 2006 AAAS

The researchers struck pay dirt when they carried out in situ hybridization (a technique featured in Chapter 22) showing where a cell–cell signal gene called *Bmp4* is expressed.

- There is a strong correlation between the amount of *Bmp4* expression when beaks are developing in young Galápagos finches and the width and depth of adult beaks (**FIGURE 25.18**).

- When the researchers experimentally increased *Bmp4* expression in young chickens, they found that beaks got wider and deeper than normal.

Similar experiments suggest that variation in alleles for a molecule called calmodulin, which is involved in calcium signaling during development, affects beak length. Based on these data, biologists suspect that alleles associated with *Bmp4* and calmodulin expression may be under selection in the population of medium ground finches that the Grants are studying. If so, the research community will have made a direct connection between natural selection on phenotypes and evolutionary change in genotypes.

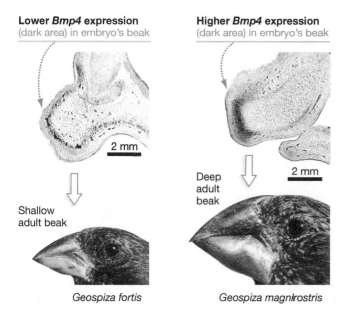

Lower *Bmp4* expression
(dark area) in embryo's beak

Higher *Bmp4* expression
(dark area) in embryo's beak

2 mm

2 mm

Deep
adult
beak

Shallow
adult beak

Geospiza fortis

Geospiza magnirostris

FIGURE 25.18 Changes in *Bmp4* Expression Change Beak Depth and Width. These micrographs are in situ hybridizations (see Chapter 22) showing the location and extent of *Bmp4* expression in young *Geospiza fortis* and *G. magnirostris*. In these and four other species that were investigated, the amount of Bmp4 protein produced correlates with the depth and width of the adult beak.

check your understanding

C Y U

If you understand that . . .

- If individuals with certain alleles produce the most offspring in a population, then those alleles increase in frequency over time. Evolution results from this process of natural selection on heritable variation.

✓ You should be able to . . .

1. List Darwin's four postulates in your own words and indicate which are related to heritable variation and which are related to differential reproductive success.

2. Explain how data on beak size and shape of Galápagos finch populations provide examples of heritable variation and differential reproductive success.

Answers are available in Appendix A.

25.5 Common Misconceptions about Natural Selection and Adaptation

Evolution by natural selection is a simple process—just the logical outcome of some straightforward postulates. Ironically, it can be extremely difficult to understand.

Research has verified that evolution by natural selection is often misunderstood. To help clarify how the process works, let's consider four of the most common types of misconceptions about natural selection, summarized in **TABLE 25.2** (on page 460).

Selection Acts on Individuals, but Evolutionary Change Occurs in Populations

Perhaps the most important point to clarify about natural selection is that during the process, individuals do not change—only the population does. During the drought, the beaks of individual finches did not become deeper. Rather, the average beak depth in the population increased over time because deep-beaked individuals produced more offspring than shallow-beaked individuals did. Natural selection acted on individuals, but the evolutionary change occurred in the characteristics of the population.

In the same way, individual *M. tuberculosis* cells did not change when rifampin was introduced to their environment. Each of these bacterial cells had the same RNA polymerase alleles throughout its life. But because the mutant allele increased in frequency in the population over time, the average characteristics of the bacterial population changed.

Natural Selection Is Not "Lamarckian" Inheritance There is a sharp contrast between evolution by natural selection and evolution by the inheritance of acquired characters—the hypothesis promoted by Jean-Baptiste de Lamarck. If you recall, Lamarck proposed that (**1**) individuals change in response to challenges posed by the environment (such as giraffes stretching their necks to reach leaves high in the treetops), and (**2**) the changed traits are then passed on to offspring. The key claim is that the important evolutionary changes occur in individuals.

In contrast, Darwin realized that individuals do not change when they are selected. Instead, they simply produce more or less offspring than other individuals do. When this happens, alleles found in the selected individuals become more or less frequent in the population.

Darwin was correct: There is no mechanism that makes it possible for natural selection to change the nature of an allele inside an individual. An individual's heritable characteristics don't change when natural selection occurs. Natural selection just sorts existing variants—it doesn't change them.

Acclimatization Is *Not* Adaptation The issue of change in individuals is tricky because individuals often *do* change in response to changes in the environment. For example, if you were to travel to the Tibetan Plateau in Asia, your body would experience oxygen deprivation due to the low partial pressure of oxygen at high elevations (see Figure 45.2). As a result, your body would produce more of the oxygen-carrying pigment hemoglobin and more hemoglobin-carrying red blood cells. Your body does not normally produce more red blood cells than it needs, because viscous (thick) blood can cause a disease—chronic mountain sickness—that can lead to heart failure.

The increase in red blood cells is an example of what biologists call **acclimatization**—a change in an individual's phenotype that occurs in response to a change in natural environmental conditions. (When this process occurs in study organisms in a laboratory, it is called **acclimation**.) Phenotypic changes due to acclimatization are not passed on to offspring, because no alleles have changed. As a result, acclimatization does not cause evolution.

Misconception	Example

"Evolutionary change occurs in organisms"

CORRECTION:
- Natural selection just sorts existing variants in organisms; it doesn't change them
- Evolutionary change occurs only in populations
- Acclimatization ≠ adaptation

Selection does not cause neck length to increase in individual giraffes, only in populations

"Adaptations occur because organisms want or need them"

CORRECTION:
- Mutation, the source of new alleles, occurs by chance
- Evolution is not goal directed or progressive
- There is no such thing as a higher or lower organism

Tapeworms are not "lower" than their human hosts, just adapted to a different environment

"Organisms sacrifice themselves for the good of the species"

CORRECTION:
- Individuals with alleles that cause self-sacrificing behavior die and do not produce offspring, so these alleles are eliminated from the population

Lemmings do not jump off cliffs into the sea to save the species

"Evolution perfects organisms"

CORRECTION:
- Some traits are nonadaptive
- Some traits cannot be optimized due to fitness trade-offs
- Some traits are limited by genetic or historical constraints

Finch beaks cannot be both deep and narrow, due to genetic constraints

In contrast, populations that have lived in Tibet for many generations are adapted to this environment through genetic changes. Among native Tibetans, for example, an allele that increases the ability of hemoglobin to hold oxygen has increased to high frequency. In populations that do not live at high elevations, this allele is rare or nonexistent. ✔ **If you understand this concept, you should be able to explain the difference between the biological definition of adaptation and its use in everyday English.**

Evolution Is Not Goal Directed

It is tempting to think that evolution by natural selection is goal directed. For example, you might hear a fellow student say that Tibetans "needed" the new hemoglobin allele so that they could survive at high altitudes, or that *M. tuberculosis* cells "wanted" or "needed" the mutant, drug-resistant allele so that they could survive and continue to reproduce in an environment that included rifampin. This purposeful change does not happen. The mutations that created the mutant alleles in both examples occurred randomly, due to errors in DNA synthesis, and they just happened to be advantageous when the environments changed.

Stated another way, mutations do not occur to solve problems. Mutations just happen. Every mutation is equally likely to occur in every environment. There is no mechanism that enables the environment to direct which mistakes DNA polymerase makes when copying genes. Adaptations do not occur because organisms want or need them.

Evolution Is Not Progressive It is often appealing to think that evolution by natural selection is progressive—meaning organisms have gotten "better" over time. (In this context, *better* usually means bigger, stronger, or more complex.) It is true that the groups appearing later in the fossil record are often more morphologically complex than closely related groups that appeared earlier. Flowering plants are considered more complex than mosses, and most biologists would agree that the morphology of mammals is more complex than that of the first vertebrates in the fossil record. But there is nothing predetermined or absolute about this tendency.

In fact, complex traits are routinely lost or simplified over time as a result of evolution by natural selection. You've already analyzed evidence documenting limb loss in snakes (Chapter 22) and whales (this chapter). Populations that become parasitic are particularly prone to loss of complex traits. For example, the tapeworm parasites of humans and other mammals have lost their sophisticated digestive tracts and mouths as a result of natural selection—tapeworms simply absorb nutrients directly from their environment.

There Is No Such Thing as a Higher or Lower Organism The nonprogressive nature of evolution by natural selection contrasts sharply with Lamarck's conception of the evolutionary process, in which organisms progress over time to higher and higher levels on a chain of being (see Figure 25.1).

Under Aristotle's and Lamarck's hypothesis, it is sensible to refer to "higher" and "lower" organisms. But under evolution by natural selection, there is no such thing as a higher or lower organism (**FIGURE 25.19**). Mosses may be a more ancient group than flowering plants, but neither group is higher or lower than the other. Mosses simply have a different suite of adaptations than do flowering plants, so they thrive in different types of environments. A human is no higher than its tapeworm parasite; each is well adapted to its environment.

Organisms Do Not Act for the Good of the Species

Consider the widely circulated story that rodents called lemmings sacrifice themselves for the good of their species. The story claims that when lemming populations are high, overgrazing is so extensive that the entire species is threatened with starvation and extinction. In response, some individuals throw themselves into the sea and drown. This lowers the overall population size and allows the vegetation to recover enough to save the species. Even though individuals suffer, the good-of-the-species hypothesis maintains that the behavior evolved because the group benefits.

The lemming suicide story is false. Although lemmings do disperse from areas of high population density to find habitats with higher food availability, they do not throw themselves into the sea.

To understand why this type of self-sacrificing behavior does not occur, suppose that certain alleles predispose lemmings to sacrifice themselves for others. But consider what happens if alleles exist that prevent this type of behavior—what biologists call

a "selfish" allele. Individuals with self-sacrificing alleles die and do not produce offspring. But individuals with selfish, cheater alleles survive and produce offspring. As a result, selfish alleles increase in frequency while self-sacrificing alleles decrease in frequency. Thus, it is not possible for self-sacrificing alleles to evolve by natural selection.

There Are Constraints on Natural Selection

Although organisms are often exquisitely adapted to their environment, adaptation is far from perfect. A long list of circumstances limits the effectiveness of natural selection; only a few of the most important are discussed here.

Nonadaptive Traits Vestigial traits such as the human coccyx (tailbone) and goose bumps do not increase the fitness of individuals with those traits. The structures are not adaptive. They exist because they were present in the ancestral population.

Vestigial traits are not the only types of structures with no or reduced function. Some adult traits exist as holdovers from structures that appear early in development. For example, human males have nipples despite the absence of mammary glands. Nipples exist in men because they form in the human embryo before sex hormones begin directing the development of male organs instead of female organs.

Perhaps the best example of nonadaptive traits involves evolutionary changes in DNA sequences. A mutation may change a base in the third position of a codon without changing the amino acid sequence of the protein encoded by that gene. Changes such as these are said to be silent. They occur due to the redundancy of the genetic code (see Chapter 16). Silent changes in DNA sequences are extremely common. But because they don't change the phenotype, they can't be acted on by natural selection and are not adaptive.

Genetic Constraints The Grants' team analyzed data on the characteristics of finches that survived the 1977 drought in the Galápagos, and the team made an interesting observation: Although individuals with deep beaks survived better than individuals with shallow beaks, birds with particularly narrow beaks survived better than individuals with wider beaks.

This observation made sense because finches crack *Tribulus* fruits by twisting them. Narrow beaks concentrate the twisting force more efficiently than wider beaks, so they are especially useful for cracking the fruits. But narrower beaks did not evolve in the population.

To explain why, the biologists noted that parents with deep beaks tend to have offspring with beaks that are both deep and wide. This is a common pattern. Many alleles that affect body size have an effect on all aspects of size—not just one structure or dimension. As a result, selection for increased beak depth overrode selection for narrow beaks, even though a deep and narrow beak would have been more advantageous.

The general point here is that selection was not able to optimize all aspects of a trait due to **genetic correlation.** Genetic correlations occur because of pleiotropy, in which a single allele affects multiple traits (see Chapter 14). In this case, selection on

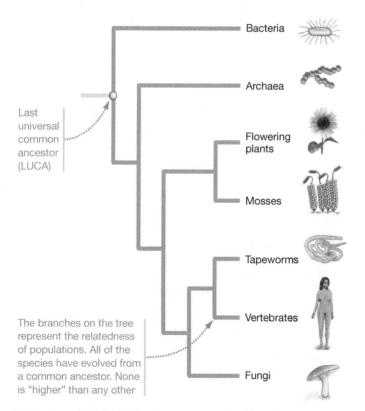

The branches on the tree represent the relatedness of populations. All of the species have evolved from a common ancestor. None is "higher" than any other

Last universal common ancestor (LUCA)

Bacteria

Archaea

Flowering plants

Mosses

Tapeworms

Vertebrates

Fungi

FIGURE 25.19 Evolution Produces a Tree of Life, Not a Progressive Ladder of Life. Under evolution by natural selection, species are related by common ancestry and all have evolved through time. (Not all branches of the tree of life are shown.)

alleles for one trait (increased beak depth) caused a correlated, though suboptimal, increase in another trait (beak width).

Genetic correlations are not the only genetic constraint on adaptation. Lack of genetic variation is also important. Consider that salamanders have the ability to regrow severed limbs. Some eels and sharks can sense electric fields. Birds can see ultraviolet light. Even though these traits would possibly confer increased reproductive success in humans, they do not exist—because humans lack the requisite genes.

Fitness Trade-offs   In everyday English, the term trade-off refers to a compromise between competing goals. It is difficult to design a car that is both large and fuel efficient, a bicycle that is both rugged and light, or a plane that is both fast and maneuverable.

In nature, selection occurs in the context of fitness trade-offs. A **fitness trade-off** is a compromise between traits, in terms of how those traits perform in the environment. During the drought in the Galápagos, for example, medium ground finches with large bodies had an advantage because they were able to chase off smaller birds from the few remaining sources of seeds. But individuals with large bodies require large amounts of food to maintain their mass; they also tend to be slower and less nimble than smaller individuals. When food is scarce, large individuals are more prone to starvation. Even if large size is advantageous in an environment, there is always counteracting selection that prevents individuals from getting even bigger.

Biologists have documented trade-offs between the size of eggs or seeds that an individual makes and the number of off-spring it can produce, between rapid growth and long life span, and between bright coloration and tendency to attract predators.

The message of this research is simple: Because selection acts on many traits at once, every adaptation is a compromise.

Historical Constraints   In addition to being constrained by genetic correlations, lack of genetic variation, and fitness trade-offs, adaptations are constrained by history. The reason is simple: All traits have evolved from previously existing traits.

Natural selection acts on structures that originally had a very different function. For example, the tiny incus, malleus, and stapes bones found in your middle ear evolved from bones that were part of the jaw and jaw support in the ancestors of mammals. These bones now function in transmitting and amplifying sound from your outer ear to your inner ear. Biologists routinely interpret these bones as adaptations that improve your ability to hear airborne sounds. But are the bones a "perfect" solution to the problem of transmitting sound from the outside of the ear to the inside? The answer is no. They are the best solution possible, given an important historical constraint. Other vertebrates have different structures involved in transmitting sound to the ear. In at least some cases, those structures may be more efficient than our incus, malleus, and stapes.

To summarize, not all traits are adaptive, and even adaptive traits are constrained by genetic and historical factors. In addition, natural selection is not the only process that causes evolutionary change. Three other processes—genetic drift, gene flow, and mutation—change allele frequencies over time (see Chapter 26). Compared with natural selection, these processes have very different consequences. You can see the Big Picture of how natural selection relates to other evolutionary processes on pages 526–527.

CHAPTER 25   REVIEW

For media, go to MasteringBiology (MB)

If you understand . . .

25.1 The Evolution of Evolutionary Thought

- Plato, Aristotle, and the Bible's book of Genesis consider species as unchanging types. This view is called typological thinking.

- Lamarck proposed a theory of evolution—that species are not static but change through time. He proposed that evolution occurs by the inheritance of acquired characteristics.

- Darwin and Wallace proposed that evolution occurs by natural selection. This was the beginning of population thinking, whereby variation among individuals is the key to understanding evolution.

✔ You should be able to compare and contrast typological thinking and population thinking.

25.2 The Pattern of Evolution: Have Species Changed, and Are They Related?

- Data on (1) the age of the Earth and the fact of extinction; (2) the resemblance of modern to fossil forms; (3) transitional features in fossils; (4) the presence of vestigial traits; and (5) change in contemporary populations show that species change through time.

- Data on (1) the geographic proximity of closely related species; (2) the existence of structural, developmental, and genetic homologies; and (3) the contemporary formation of new species support the consensus that species are related by common ancestry.

- Evidence for evolution is internally consistent, meaning that data from several independent sources are mutually reinforcing.

✔ You should be able to cite examples in support of the statement that species have changed through time and are related by common ancestry.

25.3 The Process of Evolution: How Does Natural Selection Work?

- Darwin developed four postulates that outline the process of evolution by natural selection. These postulates can be summarized by the following statement: Heritable variation leads to differential reproductive success.

- Alleles or traits that increase the reproductive success of an individual are said to increase the individual's fitness. A trait that leads to higher fitness, relative to individuals without the trait, is an adaptation. If a particular allele increases fitness and leads to adaptation, the allele will increase in frequency in the population.

✔ You should be able to explain the difference between the biological and everyday English definitions of fitness.

25.4 Evolution in Action: Recent Research on Natural Selection

- Selection by drugs on the TB bacterium and changes in the size and shape of finch beaks in the Galápagos as a result of seed availability are well-studied examples of evolution by natural selection.

- Both examples demonstrate that evolution can be observed and measured. Evolution by natural selection has been confirmed by a wide variety of studies and has long been considered to be the central organizing principle of biology.

✔ You should be able to predict how changes in *Mycobacterium tuberculosis* populations would be explained under special creation and under evolution by inheritance of acquired characters.

25.5 Common Misconceptions about Natural Selection and Adaptation

- Natural selection acts on individuals, but evolutionary change occurs in populations. Nonheritable changes that occur in individuals are not adaptations and do not result in evolution.

- Evolution is not goal directed and does not lead to perfection. There is no such thing as a higher or lower organism.

- Organisms do not act for the good of the species.

- Not all traits are adaptive, and even adaptive traits are limited by genetic and historical constraints.

✔ You should be able to discuss how adaptations such as the large brains of *Homo sapiens* and the ability of falcons to fly very fast are constrained.

(MB) MasteringBiology

1. **MasteringBiology Assignments**

   Tutorials and Activities Darwin and the Galápagos Islands; Experimental Inquiry: Did Natural Selection of Ground Finches Occur When the Environment Changed?; Natural Selection for Antibiotic Resistance; The Voyage of the *Beagle*: Darwin's Trip Around the World; Reconstructing Forelimbs

   Questions Reading Quizzes, Blue-Thread Questions, Test Bank

2. **eText** Read your book online, search, take notes, highlight text, and more.

3. **The Study Area** Practice Test, Cumulative Test, BioFlix® 3-D Animations, Videos, Activities, Audio Glossary, Word Study Tools, Art

You should be able to . . .

✔ TEST YOUR KNOWLEDGE

1. How can biological fitness be estimated?
   a. Document how long different individuals in a population survive.
   b. Count the number of healthy, fertile offspring produced by different individuals in a population.
   c. Determine which individuals are strongest.
   d. Determine which phenotype is the most common one in a given population.

2. True or false? Some traits are considered vestigial because they existed long ago.

3. What is an adaptation?
   a. a trait that improves the fitness of its bearer, compared with individuals without the trait
   b. a trait that changes in response to environmental influences within the individual's lifetime
   c. an ancestral trait—one that was modified to form the trait observed today
   d. the ability to produce offspring

4. Why does the presence of extinct forms and transitional features in the fossil record support the pattern component of the theory of evolution by natural selection?
   a. It supports the hypothesis that individuals change over time.
   b. It supports the hypothesis that weaker species are eliminated by natural selection.
   c. It supports the hypothesis that species evolve to become more complex and better adapted over time.
   d. It supports the hypothesis that species change over time.

5. Traits that are derived from a common ancestor, like the bones of human arms and bird wings, are said to be _____.

6. According to data presented in this chapter, which of the following statements is correct?
   a. When individuals change in response to challenges from the environment, their altered traits are passed on to offspring.
   b. Species are created independently of each other and do not change over time.
   c. Populations—not individuals—change when natural selection occurs.
   d. The traits of populations become more perfect over time.

7. Some biologists summarize evolution by natural selection with the phrase "mutation proposes, selection disposes." Mutation is a process that creates heritable variation. Explain what the phrase means.

8. Explain how artificial selection differs from natural selection.

9. Why don't the biggest and strongest individuals in a population always produce the most offspring?
   a. The biggest and strongest individuals always have higher fitness.
   b. In some environments, being big and strong lowers fitness.
   c. Sometimes the biggest and strongest individuals may choose to have fewer offspring.
   d. Sometimes the number of offspring is not related to fitness.

10. QUANTITATIVE The graphs in Figure 25.16 show that the average beak depth of medium ground finches increased after the drought.

However, more finches had deep beaks before the drought than after. Explain this seeming contradiction by calculating the percent of finches that survived the drought.

11. Review the section on the evolution of drug resistance in *Mycobacterium tuberculosis*.
   • What evidence do researchers have that a drug-resistant strain evolved in the patient analyzed in their study, and wasn't instead transmitted from another infected individual?
   • If the antibiotic rifampin were banned, would the mutant *rpoB* gene have lower or higher fitness in the new environment? Would strains carrying the mutation continue to increase in frequency in *M. tuberculosis* populations?

12. Describe how Darwin's four postulates would apply to a population of rabbits sharing a meadow with foxes.

13. Scientists have observed white deer mice living on coastal beaches in Florida and brown deer mice living in nearby forests. Compare and contrast how the theory of evolution by natural selection, special creation, and evolution by inheritance of acquired characters might explain this observation.

14. The average height of humans in industrialized nations has increased steadily for the past 100 years. This trait has clearly changed over time. Most physicians and human geneticists hypothesize that the change is due to better nutrition and a reduced incidence of disease. Has human height evolved?
   a. Yes, because average height has changed over time.
   b. No, because changes in height due to nutrition and reduced incidence of disease are not heritable.
   c. Yes, because height is a heritable trait.
   d. No, because height is not a heritable trait.

15. Scientists hypothesize that humans and chimpanzees diverged from a common ancestor that lived in Africa about 6–7 million years ago. What evidence would support this hypothesis?

16. The geneticist James Crow wrote that successful scientific theories have the following characteristics: (1) They explain otherwise puzzling observations; (2) they provide connections between otherwise disparate observations; (3) they make predictions that can be tested; and (4) they are heuristic, meaning that they open up new avenues of theory and experimentation. Crow added two other elements of scientific theories that he considered important on a personal, emotional level: (5) They should be elegant, in the sense of being simple and powerful; and (6) they should have an element of surprise. How well does the theory of evolution by natural selection fulfill these six criteria?

26 Evolutionary Processes

In this chapter you will learn that

Four evolutionary processes change allele frequencies in populations

by starting with a

Null hypothesis: The Hardy–Weinberg Principle   26.1

which makes five assumptions with respect to a particular gene . . .

Nonrandom mating   26.2   no

no   no   no   no

| Natural selection 26.3 | Genetic drift 26.4 | Gene flow 26.5 | Mutation 26.6 |

Four evolutionary processes

This albino sea turtle carries rare alleles that prevent pigment formation. The frequency of these alleles changes in the sea turtle population over time due to the evolutionary processes discussed in this chapter.

Since evolution is one of the five key attributes of life, understanding evolutionary processes is essential to understanding living things. How did the diversity of organisms around us (including us) come to be?

It turns out that natural selection (see Chapter 25) is only one of four processes that can shift allele frequencies in populations over time, causing evolution:

1. *Natural selection* increases the frequency of certain alleles—the ones that contribute to reproductive success in a particular environment. Natural selection is the only one of the four processes that leads to adaptation.

2. *Genetic drift* causes allele frequencies to change randomly. In some cases, drift may cause alleles that decrease fitness to increase in frequency.

This chapter is part of the Big Picture. See how on pages 526–527.

✔ When you see this checkmark, stop and test yourself. Answers are available in Appendix A.

3. *Gene flow* occurs when individuals leave one population, join another, and breed. Allele frequencies may change when gene flow occurs, because arriving individuals introduce alleles to their new population and departing individuals remove alleles from their old population.

4. *Mutation* modifies allele frequencies by continually introducing new alleles. The alleles created by mutation may be beneficial or deleterious (detrimental) or have no effect on fitness.

This chapter has two fundamental messages: Natural selection is not the only agent responsible for evolution, and each of the four evolutionary processes has different consequences for genetic variation and fitness.

The first few decades of the 1900s were pivotal for the study of evolutionary processes. Biologists began to apply Mendelian genetics (Chapter 14) to Darwinian evolution (Chapter 25), resulting in an era known as the Modern Synthesis. Evolutionary biologists, mathematicians, and geneticists collaborated to make huge leaps in *quantifying* evolution. One product of this era was a model called the **Hardy–Weinberg principle,** which serves as a mathematical null hypothesis for the study of evolutionary processes. Let's examine the logic of this model and then consider each of the four evolutionary processes in turn.

26.1 Analyzing Change in Allele Frequencies: The Hardy–Weinberg Principle

In 1908, a British mathematician, G. H. Hardy, and a German doctor, Wilhelm Weinberg, each published a major result independently. At the time, it was commonly believed that changes in allele frequency occur simply as a result of sexual reproduction—meiosis followed by the random fusion of gametes (eggs and sperm) to form offspring. Some biologists claimed that dominant alleles inevitably increase in frequency when gametes combine at random. Others predicted that two alleles of the same gene inevitably reach a frequency of 0.5.

To test these hypotheses, Hardy and Weinberg analyzed the frequencies of alleles when many individuals in a population mate and produce offspring. Instead of thinking about the consequences of a mating between two parents with a specific pair of genotypes (as you did with Punnett squares in Chapter 14), Hardy and Weinberg wanted to know what happened in an entire population when *all* of the individuals—and thus all possible genotypes—bred.

Like Darwin, Hardy and Weinberg were engaged in population thinking. A **population** is a group of individuals from the same species that live in the same area at the same time and can interbreed—and that vary in the traits they possess (Chapter 25).

The Gene Pool Concept

To analyze the consequences of matings among all of the individuals in a population, Hardy and Weinberg invented a novel approach: They imagined that all of the alleles from all the gametes produced in each generation go into a single group called the **gene pool** and then combine at random to form offspring. Something similar to this happens in species like clams and sea stars, which release their gametes into the water where the gametes mix randomly before combining to form zygotes.

To determine which genotypes would be present in the next generation and in what frequencies, Hardy and Weinberg calculated what happens when two gametes are plucked at random out of the gene pool, many times, and each of these gamete pairs then combines to form offspring. These calculations predict the genotypes of the offspring that would be produced, as well as the frequency of each genotype.

Quantitative Methods 26.1 walks through Hardy's and Weinberg's calculations by focusing on just one gene with two alleles, A_1 and A_2. The letter p is used to symbolize the frequency of A_1 alleles in the gene pool, and q is used to symbolize the frequency of A_2 alleles in the same gene pool. **FIGURE 26.1** illustrates the same calculations a little differently. The figure uses a Punnett square to predict the outcome of random mating—meaning, random combinations of all gametes in a population. (Recall that in Chapter 14 you used Punnett squares to predict the outcome of a mating between two individuals.) The outcome of this analysis is the same as in Quantitative Methods 26.1.

The resulting Hardy–Weinberg principle makes two fundamental claims:

1. If the frequencies of alleles A_1 and A_2 in a population are given by p and q, then the frequencies of genotypes A_1A_1,

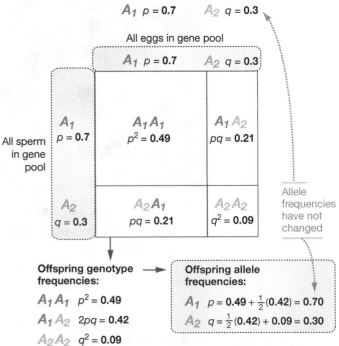

FIGURE 26.1 A Punnett Square Illustrates the Hardy–Weinberg Principle.

Hardy and Weinberg began by analyzing the simplest situation possible—where just two alleles of a particular gene exist in a population. Let's call these alleles A_1 and A_2. The letter p is used to symbolize the frequency of A_1 alleles in the gene pool and q is used to symbolize the frequency of A_2 alleles in the same gene pool. Because there are only two alleles, the two frequencies must add up to 1:

$$p + q = 1$$

Now follow the steps in **FIGURE 26.2**:

Parental Allele Frequencies

Although p and q can have any value between 0 and 1, let's suppose that the initial frequency of A_1 is 0.7 and that of A_2 is 0.3. In this gene pool, 70 percent of the gametes carry A_1 and 30 percent carry A_2.

Offspring Genotype Frequencies

Each time a gamete is involved in forming an offspring, there is a 70 percent chance that it carries A_1 and a 30 percent chance that it carries A_2. In general, there is a p chance that it carries A_1 and a q chance that it carries A_2.

Because only two alleles are present, three genotypes are possible in the offspring generation: A_1A_1, A_1A_2, and A_2A_2. What will the frequency of these three genotypes be? According to the logic of Hardy's and Weinberg's result:

- Frequency of the A_1A_1 genotype: p^2
- Frequency of the A_1A_2 genotype: $2pq$
- Frequency of the A_2A_2 genotype: q^2

The genotype frequencies in the offspring generation must add up to 1, which means that:

$$p^2 + 2pq + q^2 = 1$$

In this numerical example:

$$0.49 + 0.42 + 0.09 = 1$$

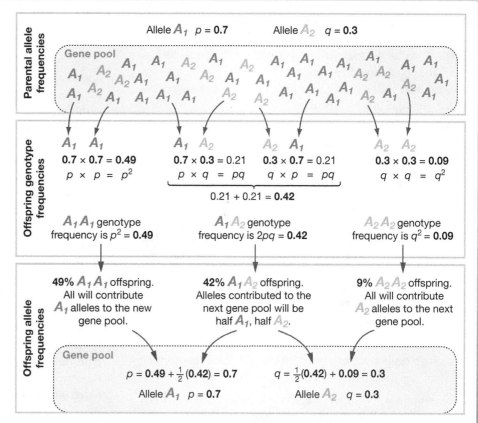

FIGURE 26.2 Deriving the Hardy–Weinberg Principle. To understand the logic behind calculating the frequency of A_1A_2 genotypes, see **BioSkills 5** in Appendix B.

Offspring Allele Frequencies

The easiest way to calculate the allele frequencies in the offspring is to imagine that they form gametes that go into a gene pool. All of the gametes from A_1A_1 individuals carry A_1, so 49 percent (p^2) of the gametes in the gene pool will carry A_1. But half of the gametes from A_1A_2 will also carry A_1, so an additional ½(0.42) = 0.21 (this is ½ × $2pq$ = pq) gametes in the gene pool will carry A_1, for a total of 0.49 + 0.21 = 0.70 or $p^2 + pq = p(p + q) = p$. Use the same logic to figure out the frequency of A_2.

In this example, the frequency of allele A_1 in the offspring generation is still 0.7 and the frequency of allele A_2 is still 0.3. Thus, the frequency of allele A_1 is still p and the frequency of allele A_2 is still q.

No change in allele frequency occurred. Even if A_1 is dominant to A_2, it does not increase in frequency. And there is no trend toward both alleles reaching a frequency of 0.5. This result is called the Hardy–Weinberg principle.

✓**QUANTITATIVE** If you understand these calculations, you should be able to: (1) calculate the frequencies of the three offspring genotypes if $p = 0.6$ and $q = 0.4$ in the parental gene pool; (2) use your answer to calculate the allele frequencies in the offspring gene pool; (3) determine whether evolution occurred.

A_1A_2, and A_2A_2 will be given by p^2, $2pq$, and q^2, respectively, for generation after generation. That is:

Allele frequencies: $p + q = 1$

Genotype frequencies: $p^2 + 2pq + q^2 = 1$

2. When alleles are transmitted via meiosis and random combinations of gametes, their frequencies do not change over time. For evolution to occur, some other factor or factors must come into play.

What are these other factors?

The Hardy–Weinberg Model Makes Important Assumptions

The Hardy–Weinberg model is based on important assumptions about how populations and alleles behave. These assumptions helped to define the four processes of evolution that can be acting on the population. In addition, the model assumes that mating is random with respect to the gene in question. Here are the five assumptions that must be met:

1. *Random mating* This condition was enforced by picking gametes from the gene pool at random. Individuals were not allowed to *choose* a mate.

2. *No natural selection* The model assumed that *all* members of the parental generation survived and contributed equal numbers of gametes to the gene pool, no matter what their genotype.

3. *No genetic drift (random allele frequency changes)* The model assumed that alleles were picked in their exact frequencies p and q, and not at some different values caused by chance—that is, the model behaved as though the population was infinitely large. For example, allele A_1 did not "get lucky" and get drawn more than 70 percent of the time.

4. *No gene flow* No new alleles were added by immigration or lost through emigration. As a result, all of the alleles in the offspring population came from the original population's gene pool.

5. *No mutation* The model didn't consider that new A_1s or A_2s or other, new alleles might be introduced into the gene pool.

The Hardy–Weinberg principle tells us what to expect if selection, genetic drift, gene flow, and mutation are not affecting a gene, *and* if mating is random with respect to that gene. Under these conditions, the genotypes A_1A_1, A_1A_2, and A_2A_2 should be in the Hardy–Weinberg proportions p^2, $2pq$, and q^2, respectively, and no evolution will occur.

How Does the Hardy–Weinberg Principle Serve as a Null Hypothesis?

Recall that a null hypothesis predicts there are no differences among the treatment groups in an experiment (see Chapter 1). Biologists often want to test whether nonrandom mating is occurring, natural selection is acting on a particular gene, or one of the other evolutionary processes is at work. In addressing questions like these, the Hardy–Weinberg principle functions as a null hypothesis.

Given a set of allele frequencies, the Hardy–Weinberg principle predicts what genotype frequencies will occur when mating is random with respect to that gene, and when natural selection, genetic drift, gene flow, and mutation are not affecting the gene. If biologists observe genotype frequencies that do not conform to the Hardy–Weinberg prediction, it means that something interesting is going on: Either nonrandom mating is occurring (which changes genotype frequencies but not allele frequencies), or allele frequencies are changing for some reason. Further research is then needed to determine which of the five Hardy–Weinberg conditions is being violated.

Let's consider two examples to illustrate how the Hardy–Weinberg principle is used as a null hypothesis: MN blood types and *HLA* genes, both in humans.

Case Study 1: Are MN Blood Types in Humans in Hardy–Weinberg Proportions? One of the first genes that geneticists could analyze in natural populations was the MN blood group of humans. Most human populations have two alleles, designated *M* and *N*, at this gene.

Because the *MN* gene codes for a protein found on the surface of red blood cells—the *M* allele codes for the M version, and the *N* allele codes for the N version—researchers could determine whether individuals are *MM, MN,* or *NN* by treating blood samples with antibodies to each protein (this technique was first introduced in Chapter 11). The *M* and *N* alleles are codominant—meaning that heterozygotes have both M and N versions of the protein on their red blood cells.

To estimate the frequency of each genotype in a population, geneticists obtain data from a large number of individuals and then divide the number of individuals with each genotype by the total number of individuals in the sample.

TABLE 26.1 shows *MN* genotype frequencies for populations from throughout the world and illustrates how observed genotype frequencies are compared with the genotype frequencies expected if the Hardy–Weinberg principle holds. The analysis is based on the following steps:

Step 1 Estimate genotype frequencies by observation—in this case, by testing many blood samples for the *M* and *N* alleles. These frequencies are given in the rows labeled "observed" in Table 26.1.

Step 2 Calculate observed allele frequencies from the observed genotype frequencies. In this case, the frequency of the *M* allele is the frequency of *MM* homozygotes plus half the frequency of *MN* heterozygotes; the frequency of the *N* allele is the frequency of *NN* homozygotes plus half the frequency of *MN* heterozygotes. (You can review the logic behind this calculation in Quantitative Methods 26.1.)

Step 3 Use the observed allele frequencies to calculate the genotypes expected according to the Hardy–Weinberg principle. Under the null hypothesis of random mating and no evolution, the expected genotype frequencies are $p^2 : 2pq : q^2$.

Step 4 Compare the observed and expected values. Researchers use statistical tests to determine whether the differences between the observed and expected genotype frequencies are small enough to be due to chance or large enough to reject the null hypothesis of no evolution and random mating.

Although using statistical testing is beyond the scope of this text (see **BioSkills 4** in Appendix B for a brief introduction to the topic), you should be able to inspect the numbers and comment on them. In these populations, for example, the observed and expected *MN* genotype frequencies are almost identical. (A statistical test shows that the small differences observed are probably due to chance.) For every population surveyed, genotypes

TABLE 26.1 The MN Blood Group of Humans: Observed and Expected Genotype Frequencies

The expected genotype frequencies are calculated from the observed allele frequencies, using the Hardy–Weinberg principle.

Population and Location	Data Type	Genotype Frequencies			Allele Frequencies	
		MM	MN	NN	M	N
Inuit (Greenland)	Observed	0.835	0.156	0.009	0.913	0.087
	Expected	0.834	0.159	0.008		
Native Americans (U.S.)	Observed	0.600	0.351	0.049	0.776	0.224
	Expected	0.602	0.348	0.050		
Caucasians (U.S.)	Observed	0.292	0.494	0.213	0.540	0.460
	Expected	0.290	0.497	0.212		
Aborigines (Australia)	Observed	0.025	0.304	0.672	0.176	0.824
	Expected	0.031	0.290	0.679		
Ainu (Japan)	Observed [Step ❶]	0.179	0.502	0.319 [Step ❷]	▭	▭
	Expected [Step ❹]	▭	▭	▭	[Step ❸]	

DATA: W. C. Boyd. 1950. Boston: Little, Brown and Company.

✔ **EXERCISE** Fill in the values for observed allele frequencies and expected genotype frequencies for the Ainu people of Japan.

at the *MN* gene are in Hardy–Weinberg proportions. As a result, biologists conclude that the assumptions of the Hardy–Weinberg model are valid for this locus.

The results imply that when these data were collected, the *M* and *N* alleles in these populations were not being affected by the four evolutionary processes and that mating was random with respect to this gene—meaning that humans were not choosing mates based on their *MN* genotype.

Before moving on, however, it is important to note that a study such as this does not mean that the *MN* gene has never been subject to nonrandom mating, or has never been under selection or genetic drift. Even if selection has been very strong for many generations, one generation of random mating and no evolution will result in genotype frequencies that conform to Hardy–Weinberg expectations.

Case Study 2: Are *HLA* Genes in Humans in Hardy–Weinberg Equilibrium?

Geneticist Therese Markow and colleagues collected data on the genotypes of 122 individuals from the Havasupai tribe native to Arizona. These biologists were studying two genes that are important in the functioning of the human immune system. More specifically, the genes that they analyzed code for proteins that help immune system cells recognize and destroy invading bacteria and viruses.

Previous work had shown that different alleles exist at both the *HLA-A* and *HLA-B* genes, and that the alleles at each gene code for proteins that recognize proteins from slightly different disease-causing organisms. Like the *M* and *N* alleles, *HLA* alleles are codominant.

As a result, the research group hypothesized that individuals who are heterozygous at one or both of these genes may have a strong fitness advantage. The logic is that heterozygous people possess a wider variety of HLA proteins, so their immune

systems can recognize and destroy more types of bacteria and viruses. They should be healthier and have more offspring than homozygous people do.

To test this hypothesis, Markow and her colleagues used their data on observed genotype frequencies to determine the frequency of each allele present. When they used these allele frequencies to calculate the expected number of each genotype according to the Hardy–Weinberg principle, they found the observed and expected values reported in **TABLE 26.2**.

When you inspect these data, notice that there are many more heterozygotes and many fewer homozygotes than expected under Hardy–Weinberg conditions. Statistical tests show it is extremely unlikely that the difference between the observed and expected numbers could occur purely by chance.

These results supported the team's prediction and indicated that one of the assumptions behind the Hardy–Weinberg

TABLE 26.2 *HLA* Genes of Humans: Observed and Expected Genotypes

The expected numbers of homozygous and heterozygous genotypes are calculated from observed allele frequencies, according to the Hardy–Weinberg principle.

Gene	Data Type	Genotype Counts (n = 122)	
		Homozygotes	Heterozygotes
HLA-A	Observed	38	84
	Expected	48	74
HLA-B	Observed	21	101
	Expected	30	92

DATA: Markow, T., P. H. Hedrick, K. Zuerlein, et al. 1993. *Journal of Human Genetics* 53: 943–952, Table 3.

principle was being violated. But which assumption? The researchers argued that mutation, gene flow, and drift are negligible in this case and offered two explanations for their data:

1. **Mating may not be random with respect to the HLA genotype.** Specifically, people may subconsciously prefer mates with *HLA* genotypes unlike their own and thus produce an excess of heterozygous offspring. This hypothesis is plausible. For example, experiments have shown that college students can distinguish each others' genotypes at genes related to *HLA* on the basis of body odor. Individuals in this study were more attracted to the smell of genotypes unlike their own. If this is true among the Havasupai, then nonrandom mating would lead to an excess of heterozygotes compared with the proportion expected under the Hardy–Weinberg principle.

2. **Heterozygous individuals may have higher fitness.** This hypothesis is supported by data collected by a different research team, who studied the Hutterite people living in South Dakota. In the Hutterite population, married women who have the same *HLA*-related alleles as their husbands have more trouble getting pregnant and experience higher rates of spontaneous abortion than do women with *HLA*-related alleles different from those of their husbands. The data suggest that homozygous fetuses have lower fitness than do fetuses heterozygous at these genes. If this were true among the Havasupai, selection would lead to an excess of heterozygotes relative to Hardy–Weinberg expectations.

Which explanation is correct? It is possible that both are. Using the Hardy–Weinberg principle as a null hypothesis allowed biologists to detect an interesting pattern in a natural population. Research continues on the question of why the pattern exists.

Now let's consider each of the processes that can violate the Hardy–Weinberg assumptions—and thus influence evolution.

check your understanding

If you understand that . . .

- The Hardy–Weinberg principle functions as a null hypothesis when researchers test whether nonrandom mating or evolution is occurring at a particular gene.

✔ **QUANTITATIVE You should be able to . . .**

Analyze whether a gene suspected of causing hypertension in humans is in Hardy–Weinberg proportions. In one study, the observed genotype frequencies were A_1A_1 0.574; A_1A_2 0.339; A_2A_2 0.087. (Note: The sample size in this study was so large that a difference of 3 percent or more in any of the observed versus expected frequencies indicated a statistically significant difference—meaning, a difference that was not due to chance.)

Answers are available in Appendix A.

26.2 Nonrandom Mating

In the Hardy–Weinberg model, gametes were picked from the gene pool at random and paired to create offspring genotypes. In nature, however, matings between individuals may not be random with respect to the gene in question. Even in species like clams that simply broadcast their gametes into the surrounding water, gametes from individuals that live close to each other are more likely to combine than gametes from individuals that live farther apart.

The most intensively studied form of nonrandom mating is called **inbreeding,** the mating between relatives. Since relatives share a recent common ancestor, individuals that inbreed are likely to share alleles they inherited from their common ancestor.

How Does Inbreeding Affect Allele Frequencies and Genotype Frequencies?

To understand how inbreeding affects populations, let's follow the fate of alleles and genotypes when inbreeding occurs. As before, focus on a single locus with two alleles, A_1 and A_2, and suppose that these alleles initially have equal frequencies of 0.5.

Now imagine that the gametes produced by individuals in the population don't go into a gene pool. Instead, individuals self-fertilize. Many flowering plants, for example, contain both male and female organs and routinely self-pollinate. Self-fertilization, or selfing, is the most extreme form of inbreeding.

As **FIGURE 26.3a** shows, homozygous parents that self-fertilize produce all homozygous offspring. Heterozygous parents, in contrast, produce homozygous and heterozygous offspring in a 1:2:1 ratio.

FIGURE 26.3b shows the outcome for the population as a whole. In this figure, the width of the boxes represents the frequency of the three genotypes, which start out at the Hardy–Weinberg ratio of $p^2 : 2pq : q^2$. Notice that the homozygous proportion of the population increases with each generation, while the heterozygous proportion is halved. At the end of the four generations illustrated, heterozygotes are rare. The same outcomes occur more slowly with less extreme forms of inbreeding.

This simple exercise demonstrates two fundamental points about inbreeding:

1. Inbreeding increases homozygosity. In essence, inbreeding takes alleles from heterozygotes and puts them into homozygotes.

2. Inbreeding itself does not cause evolution, because allele frequencies do not change in the population as a whole.

Nonrandom mating changes only genotype frequencies, not allele frequencies, so is not an evolutionary process itself. ✔ If you understand this concept, you should be able to predict how observed genotype frequencies and allele frequencies should differ from those expected under the Hardy–Weinberg principle when inbreeding is occurring.

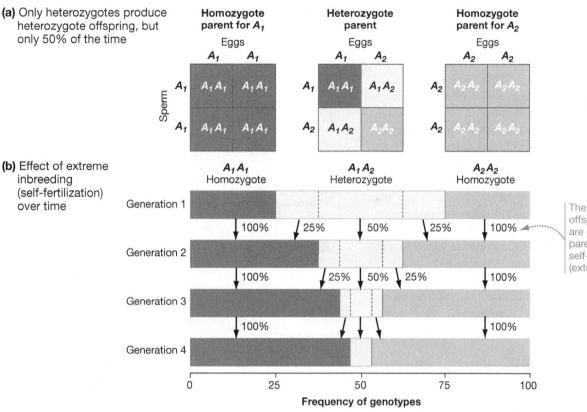

(a) Only heterozygotes produce heterozygote offspring, but only 50% of the time

Homozygote parent for A_1

Eggs
A_1 A_1

Sperm A_1: A_1A_1 A_1A_1
Sperm A_1: A_1A_1 A_1A_1

Heterozygote parent

Eggs
A_1 A_2

A_1: A_1A_1 A_1A_2
A_2: A_1A_2 A_2A_2

Homozygote parent for A_2

Eggs
A_2 A_2

A_2: A_2A_2 A_2A_2
A_2: A_2A_2 A_2A_2

(b) Effect of extreme inbreeding (self-fertilization) over time

A_1A_1 Homozygote A_1A_2 Heterozygote A_2A_2 Homozygote

Generation 1

100% 25% 50% 25% 100%

Generation 2

100% 25% 50% 25% 100%

Generation 3

100% 100%

Generation 4

Frequency of genotypes
0 25 50 75 100

The arrows represent the offspring genotypes that are produced by each parental genotype when self-fertilization occurs (extreme inbreeding)

FIGURE 26.3 Inbreeding Increases Homozygosity and Decreases Heterozygosity. (a) Heterozygous parents produce homozygous and heterozygous offspring in a 1 : 2 : 1 ratio. **(b)** The width of the boxes corresponds to the frequency of each genotype.

How Does Inbreeding Influence Evolution?

The trickiest point to grasp about inbreeding is that even though it does not cause evolution directly—because it does not change allele frequencies—it can speed the rate of evolutionary change. More specifically, it increases the rate at which natural selection eliminates recessive **deleterious** alleles—alleles that lower fitness—from a population.

Consider **inbreeding depression**—the decline in average fitness that takes place when homozygosity increases and heterozygosity decreases in a population. Inbreeding depression results from two causes:

1. *Many recessive alleles represent loss-of-function mutations.* Because these alleles are usually rare, there are normally very few homozygous recessive individuals in a population. Instead, most loss-of-function alleles exist in heterozygous individuals. The alleles have little or no effect when they occur in heterozygotes, because one normal allele usually produces enough functional protein to support a normal phenotype. But inbreeding increases the frequency of homozygous recessive individuals. Loss-of-function mutations are usually deleterious or even lethal when they are homozygous—they are quickly eliminated by selection.

2. *Many genes—especially those involved in fighting disease—are under intense selection for heterozygote advantage, a selection process that favors genetic diversity.* If an individual is homozygous at these genes, then fitness declines.

The upshot here is that the offspring of inbred matings are expected to have lower fitness than the offspring of outcrossed matings. This prediction has been verified in a wide variety of species. **FIGURE 26.4** shows results from recent efforts to reduce illness in a small population of endangered Florida panthers by introducing females from Texas. Note that the two sets of data points compare the fitnesses of offspring from non-inbred

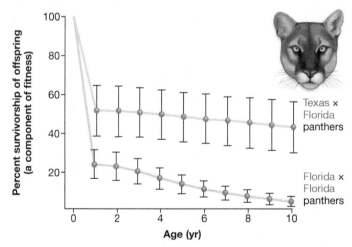

FIGURE 26.4 Inbreeding Depression Occurs in Florida Panthers. Inbreeding depression is the fitness difference between non-inbred and inbred individuals.

DATA: Johnson, W. E., E. P. Onorato, M. E. Roelke, et al. 2010. *Science* 329: 1641–1645.

Texas × Florida matings and inbred Florida × Florida matings. Inbreeding depression is represented by the vertical distance between data points at each age.

Several studies show similar results on inbreeding depression in human populations around the world. Children of first-cousin marriages consistently have a higher mortality rate than children of marriages between nonrelatives. Because inbreeding has such deleterious consequences in humans, it is not surprising that many human societies have laws forbidding marriages between individuals who are related as first cousins or closer.

In insects, vertebrates, and many other animals where inbreeding is uncommon, females often don't mate at random but actively choose certain males, and/or males compete among themselves to secure mates. This form of nonrandom mating is fundamentally different from inbreeding because it *does* lead to changes in allele frequencies in the population, and thus is a form of natural selection—called **sexual selection.** According to the Hardy–Weinberg assumptions, sexual selection violates the "no natural selection" hypothesis, as discussed in the next section.

26.3 Natural Selection

Evolution by natural selection occurs when heritable variation leads to differential success in survival and reproduction (see Chapter 25). Stated another way, natural selection occurs when individuals with certain phenotypes produce more surviving offspring than individuals with other phenotypes do. If certain alleles are associated with the favored phenotypes, they increase in frequency while other alleles decrease in frequency. The result is evolution—a violation of the assumptions of the Hardy–Weinberg model.

How Does Selection Affect Genetic Variation?

When biologists analyze the consequences of selection, they often focus on **genetic variation**—the number and relative frequency of alleles that are present in a particular population. The reason is simple: Lack of genetic variation in a population is usually a bad thing.

To understand why this is so, recall that selection can occur only if heritable variation exists in a population (Chapter 25). If genetic variation is low and the environment changes—perhaps due to the emergence of a new disease-causing virus, a rapid change in climate, or a reduction in the availability of a particular food source—no alleles that have high fitness under the new conditions are likely to be present. As a result, the average fitness of the population will decline. If the environmental change is severe enough, the population may even be faced with extinction.

Natural selection occurs in a wide variety of patterns, or modes, each with different consequences to genetic variation:

- *Directional selection* changes the average value of a trait.
- *Stabilizing selection* reduces variation in a trait.

- *Disruptive selection* increases variation in a trait.
- *Balancing selection* maintains variation in a trait.

Let's take a closer look at each of these four modes in turn.

Mode 1: Directional Selection When **directional selection** occurs, the average phenotype of a population changes in one direction.

To get a sense of how directional selection affects genetic variation, look at the top graph in **FIGURE 26.5a**, which plots the value of a trait on the *x*-axis and the number of individuals with a particular value of that trait on the *y*-axis. (In a graph like this, the *y*-axis could also plot the frequency of individuals with a

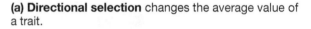

(a) Directional selection changes the average value of a trait.

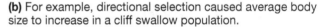

(b) For example, directional selection caused average body size to increase in a cliff swallow population.

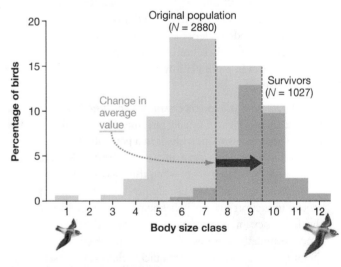

FIGURE 26.5 Directional Selection. When directional selection acts on traits that have a normal distribution, individuals at one end of the distribution experience poor reproductive success.
DATA: Brown, C. R., and M. B. Brown. 1998. *Evolution* 52: 1461–1475.

particular trait value—see **BioSkills 3** in Appendix B.) Note that the trait in question is determined by multiple genes, so it has a bell-shaped, normal distribution in this hypothetical population (Chapter 14).

The second graph in the figure shows what happens when directional selection acts on this trait. Directional selection tends to reduce the genetic diversity of populations. If directional selection continues over time, the favored alleles will eventually approach a frequency of 1.0 while disadvantageous alleles will approach a frequency of 0.0, a clear violation of the assumptions of the Hardy–Weinberg model. Alleles that reach a frequency of 1.0 are said to be fixed; those that reach a frequency of 0.0 are said to be lost. When disadvantageous alleles decline in frequency, **purifying selection** is said to occur.

Now consider data from real organisms in the wild. In 1996 a population of cliff swallows native to the Great Plains of North America endured a six-day period of exceptionally cold, rainy weather. Cliff swallows feed by catching mosquitoes and other insects in flight. Insects disappeared during this cold snap, however, and the biologists recovered the bodies of 1853 swallows that died of starvation.

As soon as the weather improved, the researchers caught and measured the body size of 1027 survivors from the same population. As the histograms in **FIGURE 26.5b** show, survivors were much larger on average than the birds that died.

Directional selection, favoring large body size, had occurred. To explain this observation, the investigators suggested that larger birds survived because they had larger fat stores and did not get as cold as the smaller birds. As a result, the larger birds were less likely to die of exposure to cold and more likely to avoid starvation until the weather warmed up and insects were again available.

If variation in swallow body size was heritable, and if this type of directional selection continued, then alleles that contribute to small body size would quickly decline in frequency in the cliff swallow population.

As it turned out in this case, directional selection was short-lived because the severe weather event was temporary. In other cases, directional selection can be more persistent, such as the directional selection that occurs during global climate change.

Mode 2: Stabilizing Selection When cliff swallows were exposed to cold weather, selection greatly reduced one extreme in the range of phenotypes and resulted in a directional change in the average characteristics of the population. But selection can also reduce both extremes in a population, as illustrated in **FIGURE 26.6a**. This mode of selection is called **stabilizing selection.** It has two important consequences: There is no change in the average value of a trait over time, and genetic variation in the population is reduced.

FIGURE 26.6b shows a classical data set in humans that illustrates stabilizing selection. Biologists who analyzed birth weights and mortality in 13,730 babies born in British hospitals in the 1940s found that babies of average size (slightly over 7 pounds)

survived best. Mortality was high for very small babies and very large babies. This is persuasive evidence that birth weight was under strong stabilizing selection in this population. Alleles associated with high birth weight or low birth weight were subject to purifying selection, and alleles associated with intermediate birth weight increased in frequency.

Mode 3: Disruptive Selection **Disruptive selection** has the opposite effect of stabilizing selection. Instead of favoring phenotypes near the average value and eliminating extreme phenotypes, it eliminates phenotypes near the average value and favors

(a) Stabilizing selection reduces the amount of variation in a trait.

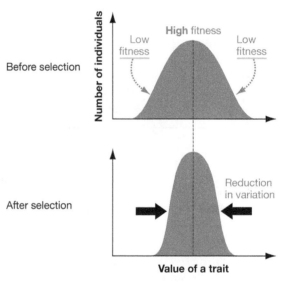

(b) For example, very small and very large babies are the most likely to die, leaving a narrower distribution of birthweights.

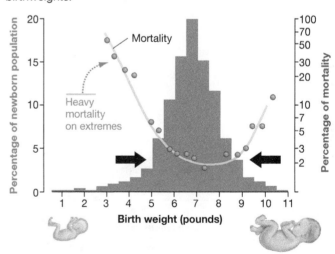

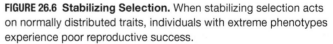

FIGURE 26.6 Stabilizing Selection. When stabilizing selection acts on normally distributed traits, individuals with extreme phenotypes experience poor reproductive success.

DATA: Karn, M. N., H. Lang-Brown, J. J. MacKenzie, et al. 1951. *Annals of Eugenics* 15: 306–322.

extreme phenotypes (**FIGURE 26.7a**). When disruptive selection occurs, the overall amount of genetic variation in the population is maintained.

Recent research has shown that disruptive selection is responsible for the striking distribution of bills of black-bellied seedcrackers (**FIGURE 26.7b**). The data plotted in the graph show that individuals with either short or very long beaks survive best and that birds with intermediate phenotypes are at a disadvantage.

In this case, the agent that causes natural selection is food. At a study site in south-central Cameroon, West Africa, a researcher found that only two sizes of seed are available to the seedcrackers: large and small. Birds with small beaks crack and eat small

(a) Disruptive selection increases the amount of variation in a trait.

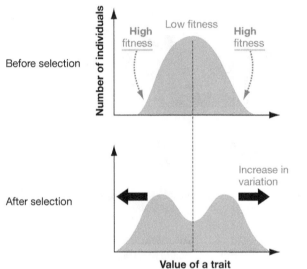

(b) For example, only juvenile black-bellied seedcrackers that had short or extremely long beaks survived long enough to breed.

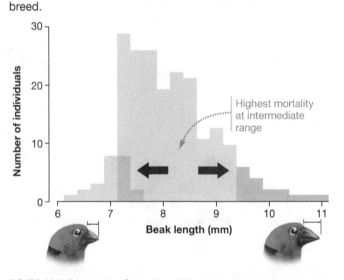

FIGURE 26.7 Disruptive Selection. When disruptive selection occurs on traits with a normal distribution, individuals with extreme phenotypes experience high reproductive success.

DATA: Smith, T. B. 1987. *Nature* 329: 717–719.

seeds efficiently. Birds with large beaks handle large seeds efficiently. But birds with intermediate beaks have trouble with both, so alleles associated with medium-sized beaks are subject to purifying selection. Disruptive selection maintains high overall variation in this population.

Disruptive selection is important because it sometimes plays a part in speciation, or the formation of new species. If small-beaked seedcrackers began mating with other small-beaked individuals, their offspring would tend to be small-beaked and would feed on small seeds. Similarly, if large-beaked individuals chose only other large-beaked individuals as mates, they would tend to produce large-beaked offspring that would feed on large seeds.

In this way, selection would result in two distinct populations. Under some conditions, the populations may eventually form two new species. (See Chapter 27 for a detailed discussion of the process of species formation, which is based on disruptive selection and other mechanisms.)

Mode 4: Balancing Selection Directional selection, stabilizing selection, and disruptive selection describe how natural selection can act on one polygenic trait in a single generation or episode. Another mode of selection, called **balancing selection,** occurs when no single allele has a distinct advantage. Instead, there is a balance among several alleles in terms of their fitness and frequency. Balancing selection occurs when:

1. Heterozygous individuals have higher fitness than homozygous individuals do, a pattern called **heterozygote advantage**. This pattern of selection is one explanation for the data in Table 26.2, where heterozygotes for the *HLA* genes have a fitness advantage compared to homozygotes. The consequence of this pattern is that genetic variation is maintained in populations.

2. The environment varies over time or in different geographic areas occupied by a population—meaning that certain alleles are favored by selection at different times or in different places. As a result, overall genetic variation in the population is maintained or increased.

3. Certain alleles are favored when they are rare, but not when they are common—a pattern known as **frequency-dependent selection.** For example, rare alleles responsible for coloration in guppies are favored because predators learn to recognize common color patterns. Alleles for common colors get eliminated; alleles for rare colors increase in frequency. As a result, overall genetic variation in the population is maintained or increased.

TABLE 26.3 summarizes the four modes of natural selection. No matter how natural selection occurs, though, its most fundamental attribute is the same: It increases fitness and leads to adaptation. Natural selection results in allele frequencies that deviate from those predicted by the Hardy–Weinberg principle because selection favors certain alleles over others. ✔ If you understand this concept, you should be able to predict how genotype frequencies differ from Hardy–Weinberg proportions under directional selection.

Mode of Selection	Effect on Phenotype	Effect on Genetic Variation
Directional selection	Favors one extreme phenotype, causing the average phenotype in the population to change in one direction.	Genetic variation is reduced.
Stabilizing selection	Favors phenotypes near the middle of the range of phenotypic variation, maintaining average phenotype.	Genetic variation is reduced.
Disruptive selection	Favors extreme phenotypes at both ends of the range of phenotypic variation.	Genetic variation is increased.
Balancing selection	No single phenotype is favored in all populations of a species at all times.	Genetic variation is maintained.

Sexual Selection

Darwin was the first to recognize that selection based on success in courtship is a mechanism of evolutionary change. Although he introduced the idea of sexual selection in *On the Origin of Species* in 1859, it was not until 12 years later that he detailed his views on sexual selection in *The Descent of Man, and Selection in Relation to Sex*.

Darwin was initially perplexed by seemingly nonadaptive traits such as the extravagantly long and iridescent trains of peacocks. Why was it adaptive for the peacock to spend energy producing a structure that would increase the peacock's vulnerability to predation? Darwin concluded that the peacock's train is adaptive because it helps the peacock to attract mates, thereby increasing its reproductive success.

The peacock example demonstrates mate choice, sometimes referred to as *inter*sexual selection—the selection of an individual of one gender for mating by an individual of the other gender. Darwin also recognized that individuals sometimes compete with one another to obtain mates. This form of selection *within* a gender is referred to as *intra*sexual selection.

Theory: The Fundamental Asymmetry of Sex Why would the extravagant trains of peacocks occur in the males but not the peahens? A. J. Bateman addressed this question in the 1940s, followed by Robert Trivers three decades later. The Bateman–Trivers theory contains an observed pattern and a hypothesized process:

- *Pattern* Sexual selection usually acts on males much more strongly than on females. Traits that attract members of the opposite sex are much more highly elaborated in males.

- *Process* The energetic cost of creating a large egg is enormous, whereas a sperm contains few energetic resources. That is, "eggs are expensive, but sperm are cheap."

In most species, females invest much more in their offspring than do males. This phenomenon is called the fundamental asymmetry of sex. It is characteristic of almost all sexual species and has two important consequences:

1. Because eggs are large and energetically expensive, females produce relatively few young over the course of a lifetime. A female's fitness is limited not by her ability to find a mate but primarily by her ability to gain the resources needed to produce more eggs and healthier young.

2. Sperm are so energetically inexpensive to produce that a male can father an almost limitless number of offspring. Thus, a male's fitness is limited not by the ability to acquire the resources needed to produce sperm but by the number of females he can mate with.

The Bateman–Trivers theory of sexual selection makes strong predictions:

- If females invest a great deal in each offspring, then they should protect that investment by being choosy about their mates. Conversely, if males invest little in each offspring, then they should be willing to mate with almost any female.

- If there are an equal number of males and females in the population, and if males are trying to mate with any female possible, then males will compete with each other for mates.

- If male fitness is limited by access to mates, then any allele that increases a male's attractiveness to females or success in male–male competition should increase rapidly in the population, violating the assumptions of Hardy–Weinberg. Thus, sexual selection should act more strongly on males than on females.

Do data from experimental or observational studies agree with these predictions? Let's consider each of them in turn.

Female Choice for "Good Alleles" If females are choosy about which males they mate with, what criteria do females use to make their choice? Recent experiments have shown that in several bird species, females prefer to mate with males that are well fed and in good health. These experiments were motivated by three key observations:

1. In many bird species, the existence of colorful feathers or a colorful beak is due to the presence of the red and yellow pigments called carotenoids.

2. Carotenoids protect tissues and stimulate the immune system to fight disease more effectively.

3. Animals usually cannot synthesize their own carotenoids, but plants can. To obtain carotenoids, animals have to eat carotenoid-rich plant tissues.

These observations suggest that the healthiest and best-nourished birds in a population have the most colorful beaks and feathers. Sick birds have dull coloration because they are using all of their carotenoids to stimulate their immune system. Poorly fed birds have dull coloration because they have few carotenoids available. By choosing a colorful male as the father of her offspring, a female is likely to have offspring with alleles that will help the offspring fight disease effectively and feed efficiently.

To test the hypothesis that females prefer colorful males, a team of researchers experimented with zebra finches (**FIGURE 26.8a**). They identified pairs of brothers and randomly assigned one brother to the treatment group and one brother to the control group. They fed the treatment group a diet that was heavily supplemented with carotenoids, and they fed the control group a diet that was similar in every way except for the additional carotenoids.

As predicted, the males eating the carotenoid-supplemented diet developed more colorful beaks than did the males fed the carotenoid-poor diet. When given a choice of perching with either of the two brothers, 9 out of the 10 females tested preferred the more-colorful male (**FIGURE 26.8b**). These results support the hypothesis that females of this species are choosy about their mates and that they prefer to mate with healthy, well-fed males.

Enough experiments have been done on other bird species to support a general conclusion: Colorful beaks and feathers, along with songs and dances and other types of courtship displays, carry the message "I'm healthy and well fed because I have good alleles. Mate with me."

Female Choice for Paternal Care
Choosing "good alleles" is not the entire story in sexual selection via female choice. In many species, females prefer to mate with males that care for young or that provide the resources required to produce eggs.

Brown kiwi females make an enormous initial investment in their offspring—their eggs routinely represent over 15 percent of the mother's total body weight (**FIGURE 26.9**)—but choose to mate with males that take over all of the incubation and other care of the offspring. It is common to find that female fish prefer to mate with males that protect a nest site and care for the eggs until they hatch. In humans and many species of birds, males provide food, protection, and other resources for rearing young.

To summarize, females may choose mates on the basis of (**1**) physical characteristics that signal male genetic quality, (**2**) resources or parental care provided by males, or (**3**) both. In some species, however, females do not have the luxury of choosing a male. Instead, competition among males is the primary cause of sexual selection.

Male–Male Competition
As an example of research on how males compete for mates, consider data from a long-term study of a northern elephant seal population breeding on Año Nuevo Island, off the coast of California.

Elephant seals feed mostly on marine fish, squid, and octopus, and spend most of the year in the water. But when females are ready to mate and give birth, they haul themselves out of the

(a) Male zebra finch

(b) Female choice for colorful beaks

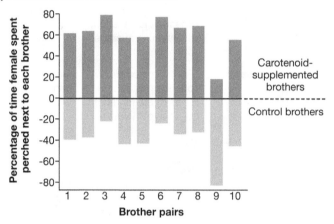

FIGURE 26.8 Female Zebra Finches Prefer Males with Colorful Beaks.

DATA: Blount, J. D., N. B. Metcalf, T. R. Birkhead, et al. 2003. *Science* 300: 125–127.

water onto land. Females prefer to give birth on islands, where newborn pups are protected from terrestrial and marine predators. Because elephant seals have flippers that are ill-suited for walking, females can haul themselves out of the water only on the few beaches that have gentle slopes. As a result, large numbers of females congregate in tiny areas to breed.

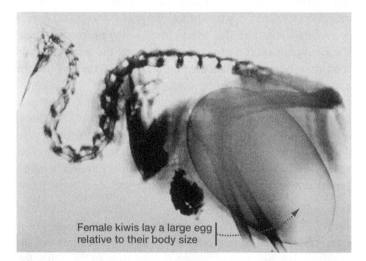

Female kiwis lay a large egg relative to their body size

FIGURE 26.9 In Many Species, Females Make a Large Investment in Each Offspring. X-ray of a female kiwi, ready to lay an egg.

Male elephant seals establish territories on breeding beaches by fighting (**FIGURE 26.10a**). A **territory** is an area that is actively defended and that provides exclusive or semi-exclusive use by the owner. Males that win battles with other males monopolize matings with the females residing in their territories. Males that lose battles are relegated to territories with fewer females or are excluded from the beach. Fights are essentially slugging contests and are usually won by the larger male. The males stand face to face, bite each other, and land blows with their heads.

Based on these observations, it is not surprising that male northern elephant seals frequently weigh 2700 kg (5940 lbs) and are over four times more massive, on average, than females. The logic here runs as follows:

- Males that dominate beaches with large congregations of females father large numbers of offspring. Males that lose fights father few or no offspring.

- The alleles of dominant males rapidly increase in frequency in the population.

- If the ability to win fights and produce offspring is determined primarily by body size, then alleles for large body size have a significant fitness advantage, leading to the evolution of large male size. The fitness advantage is due to sexual selection, and the consequence is directional selection on large body size.

FIGURE 26.10b provides evidence for intense sexual selection in males. Biologists have marked many of the individuals in the seal population on Año Nuevo to track the lifetime reproductive success of a large number of individuals. The x-axis indicates fitness, plotted as the number of offspring produced over a lifetime. The y-axis indicates the percentage of males in the population that achieved each category of offspring production (0, 1–10, and so on). As the data show, in this population a few males father a large number of offspring, while most males father few or none.

Among females, variation in reproductive success is also high, but it is much lower than in males (**FIGURE 26.10c**). In this species, most sexual selection appears to be driven more by male–male competition than by female choice.

Sexual Dimorphism Results from Sexual Selection   In elephant seals and most other animals studied, most females that survive to adulthood get a mate. In contrast, many males do not. Because sexual selection tends to be much more intense in males than females, males tend to have many more traits that function only in courtship or male–male competition. Stated another way, sexually selected traits often differ sharply between the sexes.

Sexual dimorphism (literally, "two-forms") refers to any trait that differs between males and females. Such traits range from weapons that males use to fight over females, such as antlers and

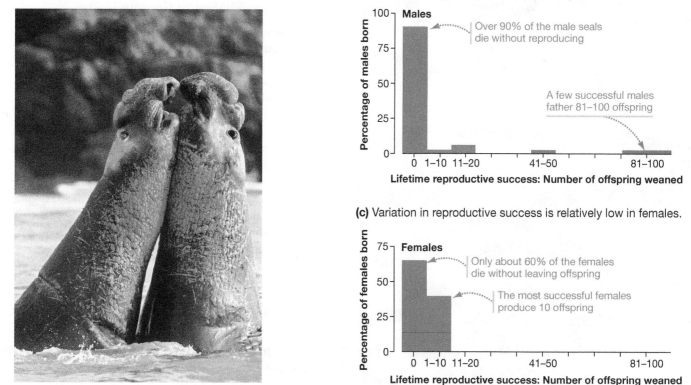

(a) Males compete for the opportunity to mate with females.

(b) Variation in reproductive success is high in males.

(c) Variation in reproductive success is relatively low in females.

FIGURE 26.10 Intense Sexual Selection in Male Elephant Seals. The histograms show that variation in lifetime reproductive success is higher in **(b)** male northern elephant seals than it is in **(c)** females.

DATA: Le Boeuf, B. J., and R. S. Peterson. 1969. *Science* 163: 91–93.

horns (**FIGURE 26.11a**), to the elaborate ornamentation and behavior used in courtship displays (**FIGURE 26.11b**). Humans are sexually dimorphic in size, distribution of body hair, and many other traits. ✔ If you understand sexual selection, you should be able to (1) define the fundamental asymmetry of sex, and (2) explain why males are usually the sex with exaggerated traits used in courtship.

Take-Home Messages Female choice and male–male competition illustrate how selection can favor certain phenotypes in a population. The adaptive alleles responsible for these phenotypes increase in frequency over time. Thus, evolution occurs and the assumptions of the Hardy–Weinberg model are violated.

Sexual selection is just one type of natural selection. All the other types, sometimes referred to collectively as **ecological (or**

(a) Red deer males use weaponry to compete for mates.

(b) Male raggiana birds of paradise display for females.

FIGURE 26.11 Sexually Selected Traits Are Used to Compete for Mates. Males often have exaggerated traits that they use in fighting or courtship. In many species, females lack these traits.

environmental) selection, favor traits that enable organisms to do things other than obtain mates—such as survive in their physical and biological environments. Different agents of natural selection can act on organisms simultaneously, sometimes favoring the same traits, other times resulting in fitness trade-offs (Chapter 25). For example, sexual selection may favor long trains in peacocks, while ecological selection may favor shorter trains that make the peacocks less vulnerable to predators. The relative importance of different agents of selection can change over time and in space.

Natural selection is the only evolutionary process that results in adaptation, but it is not the only evolutionary process that violates the Hardy–Weinberg assumptions. Let's consider what happens when random changes in allele frequency occur.

26.4 Genetic Drift

Genetic drift is defined as any change in allele frequencies in a population that is due to chance. The process is aptly named, because it causes allele frequencies to drift up and down randomly over time. When drift occurs, allele frequencies change due to blind luck—what is known in statistics as **sampling error.** Sampling error occurs when the allele frequencies of a chosen subset of a population (the sample) are different from those in the total population, by chance. Drift occurs in every population, in every generation, but especially in small populations.

Simulation Studies of Genetic Drift

To understand why genetic drift occurs, imagine a couple marooned on a deserted island. Suppose that at gene A, the wife's genotype is $A_T A_H$ and the husband is also $A_T A_H$. In this population, the two alleles are each at a frequency of 0.5.

Now suppose that the couple produce five children over their lifetime. Half of the eggs produced by the wife carry allele A_T and half carry allele A_H. Likewise, half of the sperm produced by the husband carry allele A_T and half carry allele A_H. To simulate which sperm and which egg happen to combine to produce each of the five offspring, you can flip a coin for each sperm and each egg, where tails represents allele A_T and heads represents allele A_H.

The following coin flips were done by a pair of students in a recent biology class:

	Sperm	Egg	Genotype
First offspring	A_H	A_H	$A_H A_H$
Second offspring	A_T	A_T	$A_T A_T$
Third offspring	A_T	A_H	$A_H A_T$
Fourth offspring	A_H	A_H	$A_H A_H$
Fifth offspring	A_T	A_H	$A_H A_T$

When the parents die, there are a total of 10 alleles in the population. But note that the allele frequencies have changed. In this generation, six of the 10 alleles (60 percent) are A_H; four of the 10 alleles (40 percent) are A_T. Evolution—a change in allele frequencies in a population—occurred due to genetic drift.

Instead of each allele being sampled in exactly its original frequency when offspring formed, as the Hardy–Weinberg principle assumes, a chance sampling error occurred. Allele A_H "got lucky," and allele A_T was "unlucky."

Computer Simulations   **FIGURE 26.12** shows what happens when a computer simulates the same process of random combinations in gametes over time. The program that generated the graphs combines the alleles in a gene pool at random to create an offspring generation, calculates the allele frequencies in the offspring generation, and uses those allele frequencies to create a new gene pool.

In this example, the process was continued for 100 generations. The *x*-axis on each graph plots time in generations; the *y*-axis plots the frequency of one of the two alleles present at the *A* gene in a hypothetical population.

The top graph shows eight replicates of this process with a population size of 4; the bottom graph shows eight replicates with a population of 400. Notice (**1**) the striking differences

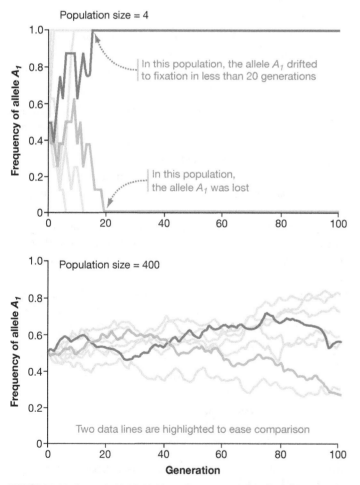

FIGURE 26.12 Genetic Drift Is More Pronounced in Small Populations than in Large Populations.

✔**EXERCISE** Draw a graph predicting what these simulation results would look like for a population size of 4000.

between the effects of drift in the small versus large population and (**2**) the consequences for genetic variation when alleles drift to fixation or loss.

Given enough time, drift can be an important factor even in large populations. For example, alleles containing silent mutations, usually in the third position of a codon, do not change the gene product (Chapter 16). As a result, most of these alleles have little or no effect on the phenotype. Yet these alleles routinely drift to high frequency or even fixation over time.

✔ If you understand genetic drift, you should be able to examine the MN blood group genotype frequencies in Table 26.1 and describe how drift could explain differences in genotype frequencies among populations. Note that there are no data indicating a selective advantage for different MN genotypes in different environments.

Key Points About Genetic Drift   These simulated matings illustrate three important points about genetic drift:

1. Genetic drift is random with respect to fitness. The changes in allele frequency that it produces are not adaptive.

2. Genetic drift is most pronounced in small populations. In the computer simulation, allele frequencies changed much less in the large population than in the small population. And if the couple on the deserted island had produced 50 children instead of five, allele frequencies in the next generation almost certainly would have been much closer to 0.5.

3. Over time, genetic drift can lead to the random loss or fixation of alleles. In the computer simulation with a population of 4, it took at most 20 generations for one allele to be fixed or lost. When random loss or fixation occurs, genetic variation in the population declines.

The importance of drift in small populations is a particular concern for conservation biologists because many populations are being drastically reduced in size by habitat destruction and other human activities. Small populations that occupy nature reserves or zoos are particularly susceptible to genetic drift. If drift leads to a loss of genetic diversity, it could darken the already bleak outlook for some endangered species.

Experimental Studies of Genetic Drift

Research on genetic drift began in the 1930s and 1940s with theoretical work that used mathematical models to predict the effect of genetic drift on allele frequencies and genetic variation. In the mid-1950s, Warwick Kerr and Sewall Wright did an experiment to determine how drift works in practice.

Kerr and Wright started with a large laboratory population of fruit flies that contained a **genetic marker**—a specific allele that causes a distinctive phenotype. In this case, the marker was the morphology of bristles. Fruit flies have bristles on their bodies that can be either straight or bent. This difference in bristle phenotype depends on a single gene. Kerr and Wright's lab population contained just two alleles—normal (straight) and "forked" (bent), designated as A_N and A_F respectively. Since the trait is

QUESTION: Does genetic drift in lab populations work as predicted by mathematical models?

HYPOTHESIS: Genetic drift causes alleles to be fixed or lost over time.

NULL HYPOTHESIS: Allele frequencies do not change; they stay in Hardy–Weinberg proportions.

EXPERIMENTAL SETUP:

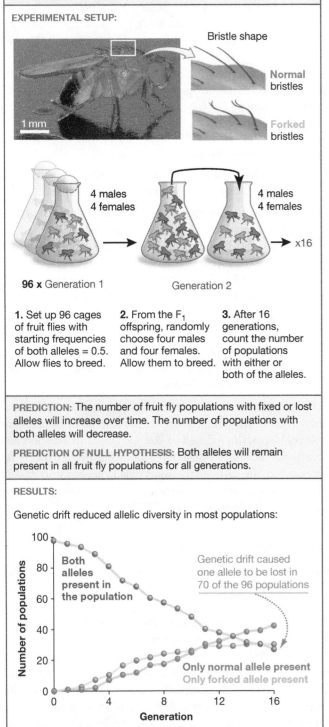

Bristle shape

Normal bristles

1 mm

Forked bristles

4 males
4 females

4 males
4 females

4 males
4 females

x16

96 x Generation 1

Generation 2

1. Set up 96 cages of fruit flies with starting frequencies of both alleles = 0.5. Allow flies to breed.

2. From the F₁ offspring, randomly choose four males and four females. Allow them to breed.

3. After 16 generations, count the number of populations with either or both of the alleles.

PREDICTION: The number of fruit fly populations with fixed or lost alleles will increase over time. The number of populations with both alleles will decrease.

PREDICTION OF NULL HYPOTHESIS: Both alleles will remain present in all fruit fly populations for all generations.

RESULTS:

Genetic drift reduced allelic diversity in most populations:

Both alleles present in the population

Genetic drift caused one allele to be lost in 70 of the 96 populations

Only normal allele present
Only forked allele present

(y-axis: Number of populations, 0 to 100)
(x-axis: Generation, 0 to 16)

CONCLUSION: Genetic drift occurs in laboratory populations as predicted by mathematical models.

sex-linked, males have only one allele (see Chapter 14). In females, the forked allele is recessive to the normal allele, but Kerr and Wright were able to distinguish homozygous females ($A_N A_N$) from heterozygotes ($A_N A_F$).

Kerr and Wright studied drift in these alleles as shown in the experimental setup in **FIGURE 26.13**:

Step 1 The researchers set up 96 small populations in their lab, each consisting of four adult females and four adult males of the fruit fly *Drosophila melanogaster*. They chose individual flies to begin these experimental populations so that the frequency of the normal and forked alleles in each of the 96 starting populations was 0.5. The two alleles do not affect the fitness of flies in the lab environment, so Kerr and Wright could be confident that if changes in the frequency of normal and forked phenotypes occurred, they would not be due to natural selection.

Step 2 After these first-generation adults bred, Kerr and Wright reared their offspring. In the offspring (F₁) generation, they randomly chose four males and four females—meaning that they simply grabbed individuals without caring whether their bristles were normal or forked—from each of the 96 offspring populations and allowed them to breed and produce the next generation.

Step 3 They repeated this procedure until all 96 populations had undergone a total of 16 generations. They then counted the number of populations that had both alleles still present, only the normal allele present, or only the forked allele present.

During the entire course of the experiment, no migration from one population to another occurred. Previous studies had shown that mutations from normal to forked bristles (and forked to normal) are rare. Thus, the only evolutionary process operating during the experiment was genetic drift. It was as if random accidents claimed the lives of all but eight individuals in each generation, so that only eight bred.

Their result? After 16 generations, both alleles were still present in only 26 of the 96 populations—significantly less than the full 96 expected by Hardy–Weinberg proportions. Forked bristles were found on all of the individuals in 29 of the experimental populations. Due to drift, the forked allele had been fixed in these 29 populations and the normal allele had been lost. In 41 other populations, however, the opposite was true: All individuals had normal bristles. In these populations, the forked allele had been lost due to chance.

The message of the study is startling: In 73 percent of the experimental populations (70 out of the 96), genetic drift had reduced allelic diversity at this gene to zero.

FIGURE 26.13 An Experiment on the Effects of Genetic Drift in Small Populations.

SOURCE: Kerr, W. E., and S. Wright. 1954. Experimental studies of the distribution of gene frequencies in very small populations of *Drosophila melanogaster*: I. Forked. *Evolution* 8: 172–177.

✔**QUESTION** Why do you think the researchers decided to start each generation with only eight individuals?

As predicted, genetic drift decreased genetic variation within populations and increased genetic differences between populations. Is drift important in natural populations as well?

What Causes Genetic Drift in Natural Populations?

The random sampling process that takes place during fertilization occurs in every population in every generation in every species that reproduces sexually. Similarly, accidents that remove individuals at random occur in every population in every generation.

It is important to realize, though, that because drift is caused by sampling error, it can occur by *any* process or event that involves sampling—not just the sampling of gametes that occurs during fertilization or the loss of unlucky individuals due to accidents. Let's consider two special cases of genetic drift, called founder effects and bottlenecks.

Founder Effects on the Green Iguanas of Anguilla When a group of individuals immigrates to a new geographic area and establishes a new population, a founder event is said to occur. If the new population is small enough, the allele frequencies in the new population are almost guaranteed to be different from those in the source population—due to sampling error. A change in allele frequencies that occurs when a new population is established is called a **founder effect** (**FIGURE 26.14a**).

In 1995, fishermen on the island of Anguilla in the Caribbean witnessed a founder event involving green iguanas. A few weeks after two major hurricanes swept through the region, a large raft composed of downed logs tangled with other debris floated onto a beach on Anguilla. The fishermen noticed green iguanas on the raft and several onshore. Because green iguanas had not previously been found on Anguilla, the fishermen notified biologists. The researchers were able to document that at least 15 individuals had arrived; two years later, they were able to confirm that at least some of the individuals were breeding. A new population had formed.

During this founder event, it is extremely unlikely that allele frequencies in the new Anguilla population of green iguanas exactly matched those of the source population, which was thought to be on the islands of Guadeloupe.

Colonization events like these have been the major source of populations that occupy islands all over the world, as well as island-like habitats such as mountain meadows, caves, and ponds. Each time a founder event occurs, a founder effect is likely to accompany it, changing allele frequencies through genetic drift.

Genetic Bottleneck on Pingelap Atoll If a large population experiences a sudden reduction in size, a population bottleneck is said to occur. The term comes from the metaphor of a few individuals of a population fitting through the narrow neck of a bottle, by chance. Disease outbreaks, natural catastrophes such as floods or fires or storms, or other events can cause population bottlenecks.

Genetic bottlenecks follow population bottlenecks, just as founder effects follow founder events. A **genetic bottleneck**

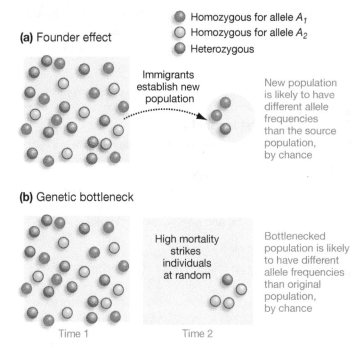

FIGURE 26.14 Two Causes of Genetic Drift in Natural Populations. The smaller the new population, the higher the likelihood that genetic drift will result in differences in allele frequencies as well as in loss of alleles.

✔ **QUANTITATIVE** The original population in (a) consists of 9 A_1A_1, 11 A_1A_2, and 7 A_2A_2 individuals (this hypothetical population is very small for simplicity). Compare the frequencies of the A_1 allele in the original and new populations.

is a sudden reduction in the number of alleles in a population (**FIGURE 26.14b**). Genetic drift occurs during genetic bottlenecks and causes a change in allele frequencies.

For an example from a natural population, consider the humans who occupy Pingelap Atoll in the South Pacific. On this island, only about 20 people out of a population of several thousand managed to survive the effects of a typhoon and a subsequent famine that occurred around 1775. The survivors apparently included at least one individual who carried a loss-of-function allele at a gene called *CNGB3*, which codes for a protein involved in color vision.

The *CNGB3* allele is recessive, and when it is homozygous it causes a serious vision deficit called achromatopsia. People with this condition have poor vision and are either totally or almost totally color-blind. The condition is extremely rare in most populations, and the frequency of the *CNGB3* allele is estimated to be under 1.0 percent.

In the population that survived the Pingelap Atoll disaster, however, the loss-of-function allele was at a frequency of about 1/40, or 2.5 percent. If the allele was at the typical frequency of 1.0 percent or less before the population bottleneck, then a large frequency change occurred during the bottleneck, due to drift.

In today's population on Pingelap Atoll, over 1 in 20 people are afflicted with achromatopsia, and the allele that causes the affliction is at a frequency of well over 20 percent. Because the loss-of-function allele is extremely unlikely to be favored by directional selection or heterozygote advantage, researchers hypothesize that the frequency of the allele in this small population has continued to increase over the past 230 years due to drift.

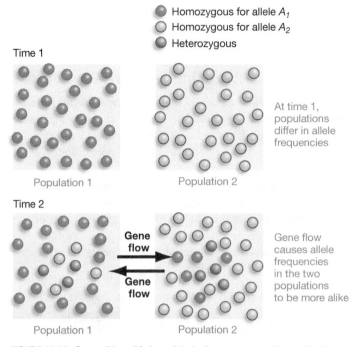

- Homozygous for allele A_1
- Homozygous for allele A_2
- Heterozygous

Time 1

Population 1   Population 2

At time 1, populations differ in allele frequencies

Time 2

Gene flow

Gene flow

Population 1   Population 2

Gene flow causes allele frequencies in the two populations to be more alike

FIGURE 26.15 Gene Flow Makes Allele Frequencies More Similar between Populations. Gene flow can occur in one or both directions. If gene flow continues and no selection occurs, allele frequencies will eventually be identical.

26.5 Gene Flow

When an individual leaves one population, joins another, and breeds, **gene flow** is said to occur—the movement of alleles between populations. Note that while allele flow might be a more apt description, gene flow is the term that evolutionary biologists traditionally use. Also note that while organisms can *emigrate* from a source population or *immigrate* to a new population, the movement of their alleles is called gene flow.

As an evolutionary process, gene flow usually has one outcome: It equalizes allele frequencies between the source population and the recipient population. When alleles move from one population to another, the populations tend to become more alike. To capture this point, biologists say that gene flow homogenizes allele frequencies among populations (**FIGURE 26.15**).

Measuring Gene Flow between Populations

The presence or absence of gene flow has particularly important implications for the conservation of threatened and endangered species. Numerous studies have documented the decline of gene flow between wild populations that have been isolated from one another—for example, by habitat fragmentation. Many studies have also documented the effects of gene flow between wild populations and captive populations.

For example, the captive breeding of fish is increasing around the world as wild populations are being depleted. In some cases, wild fish are used to start captive populations, which are then kept isolated in "farms" until they go to market—except when they escape. In other cases, captive-bred fish are purposefully released into the wild in an effort to supplement the size of wild

populations. What are the effects of gene flow between captive-bred populations and wild populations?

A team of biologists recently studied steelhead trout (*Oncorhynchus mykiss*) in the Hood River of Oregon to answer this question (**FIGURE 26.16a**). Some of the trout in the Hood River are wild, while others were raised in a hatchery and released to supplement the diminishing wild population. The researchers were able to catch, sample, and release all of the steelhead trout in the Hood River each year for three years by trapping them in a dam near the mouth of the river as the fish traveled upstream to their wintering streams.

The researchers extracted DNA from tissue samples and calculated genotypes using eight microsatellite alleles (see Chapter 21) to determine whether the parents of each fish were wild or captive-bred. The team then compared the reproductive fitness—the number of surviving adult offspring—of the trout in three groups:

1. Individuals with two wild parents (Wild × Wild)
2. Individuals with one wild parent and one captive-bred parent (Wild × Captive)
3. Individuals with two captive-bred parents (Captive × Captive)

The graph in **FIGURE 26.16b** shows the fitness results for female steelhead trout. Individuals with one or two captive-bred parents are assigned a value from 0 to 1 relative to the fitness of trout with two wild parents (fitness = 1). Individuals with one captive-bred parent have 16 percent lower fitness than wild trout on average, while individuals with two captive-bred parents have significantly lower fitness, 38 percent lower than wild-bred trout,

(a) Wild steelhead trout populations are declining

(b) Captive-bred trout reduce the fitness of wild populations

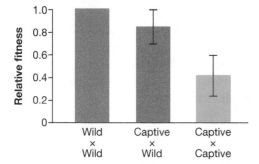

FIGURE 26.16 Gene Flow Reduces Fitness in a Population of Steelhead Trout. In this study, the fitness of female steelhead trout with one or two captive-bred parents is shown relative to females with two wild parents. Data for males are comparable (not shown).

DATA: Araki, H., B. Cooper, and M. S. Blouin. 2009. *Biology Letters* 5(5): 621–624.

on average. The researchers observed similar results for males (not shown).

These data demonstrate that gene flow is occurring from the captive-bred population to the wild population and is causing a reduction in fitness in that population. Related research on farmed Atlantic salmon in Ireland demonstrated that farmed salmon produce smaller eggs, spawn at different times, and have different predator-avoidance behaviors than wild salmon. When farmed salmon were introduced into wild populations, the reproductive success of the wild population decreased.

The conclusion of these studies on steelhead trout and Atlantic salmon is that gene flow between captive-bred and wild populations reduces fitness in the wild populations. As a result, efforts to augment wild populations with captive-bred fish may ultimately result in a *decline* in population size—contrary to the intentions of fisheries biologists.

Gene Flow Is Random with Respect to Fitness

It is not true, though, that gene flow always reduces fitness in the receiving population. If a population has lost alleles due to genetic drift, then the arrival of new alleles via gene flow should increase genetic diversity. If increased genetic diversity results in better

resistance to infections by bacteria or viruses or other parasites, for example, gene flow would increase the average fitness of individuals. This was the result when gene flow was used to aid an endangered population of the Florida panther (see Figures 26.4 and 57.14).

Gene flow is random with respect to fitness—the arrival or departure of alleles can increase or decrease average fitness, depending on the situation. But in every case, movement of alleles between populations tends to reduce their genetic differences.

This latter generalization is particularly important in our own species right now. Large numbers of people from Africa, the Middle East, Mexico, Central America, and Asia are immigrating to the countries of the European Union and the United States. Because individuals from different cultural and ethnic groups are intermarrying and having offspring, allele frequencies are becoming more similar across human populations.

26.6 Mutation

To appreciate the role of mutation as an evolutionary force, let's return to one of the central questions that biologists ask about an evolutionary process: How does it affect genetic variation in a population? Recall that:

- Natural selection often favors certain alleles and leads to a decrease in overall genetic variation.

- Genetic drift tends to decrease genetic diversity over time, as alleles are randomly lost or fixed.

- Gene flow increases genetic diversity in a recipient population if new alleles arrive with immigrating individuals. But gene flow may decrease genetic variation in the source population if alleles leave with emigrating individuals.

If most of the evolutionary processes lead to a loss of genetic diversity over time, what restores it? In sexually reproducing organisms, independent assortment and recombination (crossing over) are major sources of genetic diversity (see Chapter 13). But these processes create new combinations of existing alleles. Where do entirely new alleles come from? The answer to this question is **mutation.**

Mutations can occur in a number of ways (Chapters 16 and 21):

- *Point mutations* If a change in nucleotide sequence occurs in a stretch of DNA that codes for a protein, the new allele may result in a polypeptide with a novel amino acid sequence. If the mutation occurs in a stretch of DNA that codes for regulatory RNA, the new allele may result in a change in regulation of the expression of other alleles.

- *Chromosome-level mutations* One consequence of chromosome mutation is gene duplication, which increases the number of copies of a gene. If duplicated genes diversify via point mutations, they can lose their function or create new alleles.

- *Lateral gene transfer (also known as horizontal gene transfer)* New studies suggest that the transfer of genes from one species to another, rather than from parent to offspring, might be a more important source of genetic variation than previously realized (Chapter 21).

Because errors and chromosome damage are inevitable, mutation constantly introduces new alleles into populations in every generation. Mutation is an evolutionary process that increases genetic diversity in populations.

Even though it consistently leads to an increase in genetic diversity in a population, mutation is random with respect to the affected allele's impact on the fitness of the individual. Changes in the makeup of chromosomes or in specific DNA sequences do not occur in ways that tend to increase fitness or decrease fitness. Mutation just happens.

But because most organisms are well adapted to their current habitat, random changes in genes usually result in products that do not work as well as the alleles that currently exist. Stated another way, most mutations in sequences that code for a functional protein or RNA result in deleterious alleles, which lower fitness. Deleterious alleles tend to be eliminated by purifying selection.

On rare occasions, however, mutation in these types of sequences produces a **beneficial** allele—an allele that allows individuals to produce more offspring. Beneficial alleles should increase in frequency in the population due to natural selection.

Because mutation produces new alleles, it can in principle change the frequencies of alleles through time. But does mutation *alone* occur often enough to make it an important factor in changing allele frequencies? The short answer is no.

Mutation as an Evolutionary Process

To understand why mutation is not a significant mechanism of evolutionary change by itself, consider that the highest mutation rates that have been recorded at individual genes in humans are on the order of 1 mutation in every 10,000 gametes produced by an individual. This rate means that for every 10,000 alleles produced, on average one will have a mutation at the gene in question.

When two gametes combine to form an offspring, then, at most about 1 in every 5000 offspring will carry a mutation at a particular gene. Now suppose that 195,000 humans live in a population, that 5000 offspring are born one year, and that at the end of that year, the population numbers 200,000. Humans are diploid, so in a population this size there are, in total, 400,000 copies of each gene. Only one of them is a new allele created by mutation, however. Over the course of a year, the allele frequency change introduced by mutation is 1/400,000, or 0.0000025 (2.5×10^{-6}). At this rate, it would take 4000 years for mutation to produce a change in allele frequency of 1 percent.

These calculations support the conclusion that mutation does little on its own to change allele frequencies. Although mutation can be a significant evolutionary process in bacteria and archaea, which have extremely short generation times, mutation in eukaryotes rarely causes a change from the genotype frequencies expected under the Hardy–Weinberg principle. As an evolutionary process, mutation is slow compared with selection, genetic drift, and gene flow.

However, mutation can have a very large effect on evolution when *combined* with genetic drift, gene flow, and selection. Let's consider two examples.

Experimental Studies of Mutation

Consider a lab experiment designed by Richard Lenski and colleagues to evaluate the role that mutation plays over many generations.

Experimental Evolution Lenski's group focused on *Escherichia coli*, a bacterium that is a common resident of the human intestine. To begin, they set up a large series of populations, each founded with a single cell, and allowed them to replicate for over four years—about 10,000 generations. The strain of *E. coli* used in the experiment is completely asexual and reproduces by cell division. Thus, mutation was the only source of genetic variation in these populations.

The biologists saved a sample of cells from each population at regular intervals during the experiment and stored them in a freezer. Because frozen *E. coli* cells resume growth when they are thawed, the frozen cells serve as an archive of individuals from different generations.

Were cells from the older and newer generations of each population different? Lenski's group used competition experiments to address this question. They grew cells from two different generations on the same plate and compared their growth rates. The populations of cells that were more numerous had grown the fastest, meaning that they were better adapted to the experimental environment.

In this way the researchers could measure the fitness of descendant populations relative to ancestral populations. Relative fitness values greater than 1 meant that recent-generation cells outnumbered older-generation cells following the competition.

Fitness Increased in Fits and Starts The data from the competition experiments are graphed in **FIGURE 26.17**. Notice that relative fitness increased dramatically—almost 30 percent—over time. But notice also that fitness increased in fits and starts. This pattern is emphasized by the solid line on the graph, which represents a mathematical function fitted to the data points.

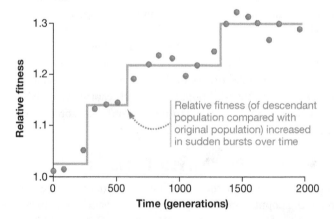

FIGURE 26.17 Evidence of Mutation in Lab Populations of *E. coli*.

DATA: Elena, S. F., V. S. Cooper, and F. E. Lenski. 1996. *Science* 272: 1802–1804.

What caused this stair-step pattern? Lenski's group hypothesized that genetic drift was relatively unimportant in this experiment because population sizes were so large. Instead, they proposed that each jump was caused by a novel mutation that conferred a fitness benefit under selection. Their interpretation was that cells that happened to have the beneficial mutation grew rapidly and came to dominate the population.

After a beneficial mutation occurred, the fitness of the population stabilized—sometimes for hundreds of generations—until another random but beneficial mutation occurred and produced another jump in fitness. These results demonstrate the combined effects of mutation and natural selection.

Studies of Mutation in Natural Populations

Lenski's experiment demonstrates the effect of cumulative mutations in laboratory populations. Now consider a recent study showing how several forms of mutation have combined with natural selection to create color variations, or polymorphisms, in pea aphids.

Lateral Gene Transfer Pea aphids (*Acyrthosiphon pisum*) are small insects that feed on plant sap. They occur in two colors in the wild, red and green, and both colors coexist within populations (**FIGURE 26.18a**). The two phenotypes are maintained in the population due to frequency-dependent selection—ladybird beetles are more likely to prey on red aphids, whereas parasitoid wasps are more likely to lay their eggs in green aphids. The balancing selection on both colors preserves genetic variation in the populations.

The color of aphids is determined by carotenoid pigments, the same group of pigments that give zebra finches their bright orange beaks. Finches and other animals get their carotenoid pigments from the food they eat, mostly from plants.

But there is a twist. Pea aphids do *not* acquire their carotenoids from the plant sap they eat. So where do the pigments come from? Researchers recently examined several bacteria associated with pea aphids and concluded that the carotenoids did not originate from these symbionts either. Instead, other researchers found that the aphids are generating their *own* carotenoids—the first animals ever discovered to have this ability.

If the ancestors of aphids did not have the genes that code for the necessary enzymes for carotenoid biosynthesis, how did the pea aphids obtain this pathway? The answer is by mutation, more specifically by lateral gene transfer—from the genome of a fungal symbiont to the genome of a recent ancestor of the pea aphids. This result was surprising—clear evidence of lateral gene transfer from one eukaryote to another.

Gene Duplication Lateral gene transfer is only part of the mutation story in pea aphids. Carotenoids are a family of molecules with similar pigment and a number of intermediate forms. Two types of enzymes are primarily responsible for the biosynthesis of these molecules in both pea aphids and their fungal ancestor.

A comparison of aphid and fungal genome sequences suggests that after the fungal genes for these two types of enzymes

(a) Red–green color polymorphism in pea aphids

(b) Origin of genes for carotenoid synthesis enzymes in aphids

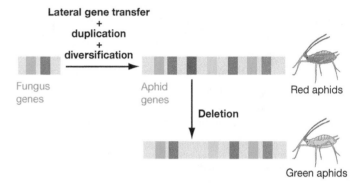

FIGURE 26.18 Evidence of Mutation in Pea Aphids.

were transferred to aphids, they underwent further mutations—duplications, sequence diversification by point mutations, and deletion. As a result, red pea aphids have the enzymes necessary to synthesize yellow, green, and red carotenoid pigments, while green pea aphids have the enzymes necessary to synthesize only the yellow and green ones (**FIGURE 26.18b**). The deletion of a gene in the green aphid genome illustrates an important point: Sometimes a loss-of-function mutation can be adaptive. In this case, being green helps aphids to avoid predation by ladybird beetles.

Take-Home Messages

The research on mutations in *E. coli* populations in the lab and the origin of color polymorphism in pea aphids reinforces three fundamental messages about the role of mutation in evolution.

1. Mutation is the ultimate source of genetic variation. Crossing over and independent assortment shuffle existing alleles into new combinations, but only mutation creates new alleles. Mutations just happen—organisms cannot create mutations because they "want" or "need" them.

2. If mutation did not occur, evolution would eventually stop. Recall that natural selection and genetic drift tend to eliminate alleles. Without mutation, eventually there would be no variation for selection and drift to act on.

	Definition/Description	Effect on Genetic Variation	Effect on Average Fitness
Natural selection	Certain alleles are favored	Can maintain, increase, or reduce genetic variation	Can produce adaptation, increasing fitness
Genetic drift	Random changes in allele frequencies; most important in small populations	Tends to reduce genetic variation via loss or fixation of alleles	Random with respect to fitness; usually reduces average fitness
Gene flow	Movement of alleles between populations; reduces differences between populations	May increase genetic variation by introducing new alleles; may decrease it by removing alleles	Random with respect to fitness; may increase or decrease average fitness by introducing high- or low-fitness alleles
Mutation	Production of new alleles	Increases genetic variation by introducing new alleles	Random with respect to fitness; most mutations in coding sequences lower fitness

3. Mutation *alone* is usually inconsequential in changing allele frequencies at a particular gene. However, when considered across the genome and when combined with natural selection, genetic drift, and gene flow, mutation becomes an important evolutionary process.

TABLE 26.4 summarizes these points and similar conclusions about the four evolutionary processes. Each of the four evolutionary processes has different consequences for allele frequencies, all of them violating Hardy–Weinberg predictions. These processes interact to create new species—that is, new branches on the tree of life (Chapter 27). The ultimate result is biological diversity (Chapter 28 and Unit 6). You can see how nonrandom mating and the four evolutionary processes fit into the Big Picture of Evolution on pages 526–527.

CHAPTER 26 REVIEW

For media, go to MasteringBiology (MB)

If you understand . . .

26.1 Analyzing Change in Allele Frequencies: The Hardy–Weinberg Principle

- The Hardy–Weinberg principle played an important role in the synthesis of Mendelian genetics and Darwinian evolution.

- The Hardy–Weinberg principle can serve as a null hypothesis in evolutionary studies because it predicts what genotype and allele frequencies are expected to be if mating is random with respect to the gene in question and if none of the four evolutionary processes is operating on that gene.

✔ QUANTITATIVE You should be able to write out the Hardy–Weinberg equations for allele and genotype frequencies and calculate the genotype frequencies expected if the frequency of A_1 is 0.2.

26.2 Nonrandom Mating

- Nonrandom mating changes only genotype frequencies, not allele frequencies, so is not an evolutionary process itself.

- Inbreeding, or mating among relatives, is a form of nonrandom mating. It leads to an increase in homozygosity and a decrease in heterozygosity.

- Inbreeding can accelerate natural selection and can cause inbreeding depression.

✔ You should be able to predict how extensive inbreeding during the 1700s and 1800s affected the royal families of Europe.

26.3 Natural Selection

- Natural selection is the only evolutionary process that produces adaptation.

- Directional selection favors phenotypes at one end of a distribution. It decreases allelic diversity in populations.

- Stabilizing selection eliminates phenotypes with extreme characteristics. It decreases allelic diversity in populations.

- Disruptive selection favors extreme phenotypes and thus maintains genetic variation in populations. Disruptive selection sometimes leads to the formation of new species.

- Balancing selection occurs when no single phenotype is favored; there is a balance among alleles in terms of fitness and frequency. Balancing selection preserves genetic variation.

- Sexual selection is a type of natural selection that leads to the evolution of traits that help individuals attract mates. It usually has a stronger effect on males than on females.

✔ You should be able to explain why natural selection violates the Hardy–Weinberg principle.

26.4 Genetic Drift

- Genetic drift causes random changes in allele frequencies.
- Genetic drift is particularly important in small populations, and it tends to reduce overall genetic diversity.
- Genetic drift can result from random fusion of gametes at fertilization, founder events, and population bottlenecks.

✔ You should be able to suggest how genetic drift could be important to the management of endangered species.

26.5 Gene Flow

- Gene flow equalizes allele frequencies between populations.
- Gene flow can introduce alleles from one population to another when individuals migrate among populations.
- The introduced alleles may have a beneficial, neutral, or deleterious effect.

✔ You should be able to suggest how gene flow could be important to the management of endangered species.

26.6 Mutation

- Mutation is the only evolutionary process that creates new alleles. They may be beneficial, neutral, or deleterious.
- Mutation occurs too infrequently to be a major cause of change in allele frequency alone, but it is important when combined with natural selection, genetic drift, and gene flow.

✔ You should be able to suggest how mutation could be important to the management of endangered species.

(MB) MasteringBiology

1. MasteringBiology Assignments

Tutorials and Activities Causes of Evolutionary Change, Hardy–Weinberg Principle, Mechanisms of Evolution, Three Modes of Natural Selection

Questions Reading Quizzes, Blue-Thread Questions, Test Bank

2. eText Read your book online, search, take notes, highlight text, and more.

3. The Study Area Practice Test, Cumulative Test, BioFlix® 3-D Animations, Videos, Activities, Audio Glossary, Word Study Tools, Art

You should be able to . . .

✔ TEST YOUR KNOWLEDGE
Answers are available in Appendix A

1. In what sense is the Hardy–Weinberg principle a null hypothesis?

2. Why isn't inbreeding considered an evolutionary process?
   a. It does not change genotype frequencies.
   b. It does not change allele frequencies.
   c. It does not occur often enough to be important in evolution.
   d. It does not violate the assumptions of the Hardy–Weinberg principle.

3. Why is genetic drift aptly named?
   a. It causes allele frequencies to drift up or down randomly.
   b. It occurs when alleles from one population drift into another.
   c. It occurs when mutations drift into a genome.
   d. It occurs when populations drift into new habitats.

4. What does it mean when an allele reaches "fixation"?
   a. It is eliminated from the population.
   b. It has a frequency of 1.0.

   c. It is dominant to all other alleles.
   d. It is adaptive.

5. True or false? Gene flow can either increase or decrease the average fitness of a population.

6. Mutation is the ultimate source of genetic variability. Why is this statement correct?
   a. DNA polymerase (the enzyme that copies DNA) is remarkably accurate.
   b. "Mutation proposes and selection disposes."
   c. Mutation is the only source of new alleles.
   d. Mutation occurs in response to natural selection. It generates the alleles that are required for a population to adapt to a particular habitat.

✔ TEST YOUR UNDERSTANDING
Answers are available in Appendix A

7. **QUANTITATIVE** In a population of 2500, how many babies would you expect to have cystic fibrosis, a homozygous recessive condition, if the frequency of the dominant allele is 0.9 and the population is at Hardy–Weinberg equilibrium?
   a. $0.9 \times 2500 = 2025$
   b. $2 \times 0.9 \times 0.1 \times 2500 = 800$
   c. $0.9 \times 0.1 \times 2500 = 400$
   d. $0.1 \times 0.1 \times 2500 = 25$

8. Suggest why inbreeding could cause recessive deleterious alleles for cystic fibrosis to be "purged" from a population.

9. Determine what is incorrect in the following statement: Red aphids mutated their genes so that they could be green and avoid predation by ladybird beetles.

10. Why does sexual selection often lead to sexual dimorphism?

11. Consider an allele that increases reproductive success in elephant seal males versus an allele that increases reproductive success in females. Which allele will increase in frequency faster, and why?

12. Draw a small concept map (**BioSkills 15**) showing how selection, genetic drift, gene flow, and mutation relate to genetic variation.

13. QUANTITATIVE In humans, albinism is caused by loss-of-function mutations in genes involved in the synthesis of melanin, the dark pigment in skin. Only people homozygous for a loss-of-function allele (genotype *aa*) have the albino phenotype. In Americans of northern European ancestry, albino individuals are present at a frequency of about 1 in 10,000 (or 0.0001). Assuming that genotypes are in Hardy–Weinberg proportions, what is the frequency of Caucasians in the United States who carry an allele for albinism?

14. A group of researchers presented artificial calls of the male cricket *Teleogryllus commodus* to female crickets in the lab to measure selection for male calls. They used artificial calls so that they could vary properties such as length of the pause between calls and number of trills in each call. When positive selection was plotted as a function of call characteristics, the shapes of the selection curves started low, peaked in the middle, and ended low. What kind of selection is occurring?
a. sexual selection
b. balancing selection
c. sexual selection and stabilizing selection
d. sexual selection and balancing selection

15. Suppose you were studying several species of human. In one, males never lifted a finger to help females raise children. In another, males provided just as much parental care as females except for actually carrying the baby during pregnancy. How does the fundamental asymmetry of sex compare in the two species? How would you expect sexual dimorphism to compare between the two species?

16. You are a conservation biologist charged with creating a recovery plan for an endangered species of turtle. The turtle's habitat has been fragmented by suburbanization and highway construction into small, isolated, but protected areas. Some evidence indicates that certain turtle populations are adapted to typical freshwater marshes, whereas others are adapted to acidic wetlands or salty habitats. Further, some turtle populations number less than 25 breeding adults, making genetic drift and inbreeding a major concern. In creating a recovery plan, the tools at your disposal are captive breeding, the capture and transfer of adults to create gene flow, or the creation of habitat corridors between wetlands to make migration possible. How would you use gene flow to help this species?

The Big Picture

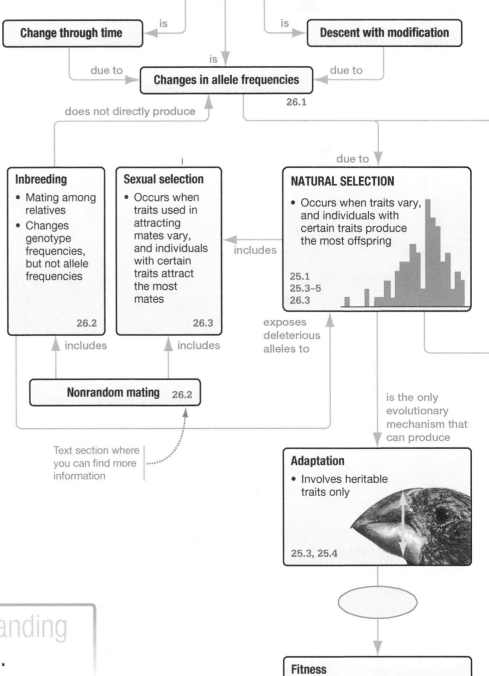

Geneticist and evolutionary biologist Theodosius Dobzhansky said that "Nothing in biology makes sense except in the light of evolution." Use this concept map to study how ideas introduced in Unit 5 fit together.

The key is to connect the four evolutionary processes that work at the level of populations—natural selection, genetic drift, mutation, and gene flow—to processes, events, and outcomes at higher levels of organization: speciation, adaptive radiation, mass extinction, and the tree of life.

It's all about changes in allele frequencies. Over time, small changes that occur between populations lead to large changes that distinguish major lineages on the tree of life.

Note that each box in the concept map indicates the chapter and section where you can go for review. Also, be sure to do the blue exercises in the Check Your Understanding box below.

EVOLUTION

Change through time — is →

is ↓

← is — Descent with modification

Changes in allele frequencies 26.1

due to · due to · due to

does not directly produce

Inbreeding
- Mating among relatives
- Changes genotype frequencies, but not allele frequencies

26.2

Sexual selection
- Occurs when traits used in attracting mates vary, and individuals with certain traits attract the most mates

26.3

NATURAL SELECTION
- Occurs when traits vary, and individuals with certain traits produce the most offspring

25.1
25.3–5
26.3

includes

includes · includes

Nonrandom mating 26.2

Text section where you can find more information

exposes deleterious alleles to

is the only evolutionary mechanism that can produce

Adaptation
- Involves heritable traits only

25.3, 25.4

usually reduces

Fitness
- Measured by number of viable, fertile offspring produced

25.3, 25.5 26.1–6

check your understanding

(C) (Y) (U)

If you understand the big picture . . .

✔ You should be able to . . .

1. Draw a circle around the processes that violate the Hardy–Weinberg principle.

2. Fill in the blue ovals with appropriate linking verbs or phrases.

3. Add a box for "Fossil record" with appropriate connections.

4. Draw arrows linking genetic drift, mutation, and gene flow to the appropriate box using the linking phrase "is random with respect to."

Answers are available in Appendix A.

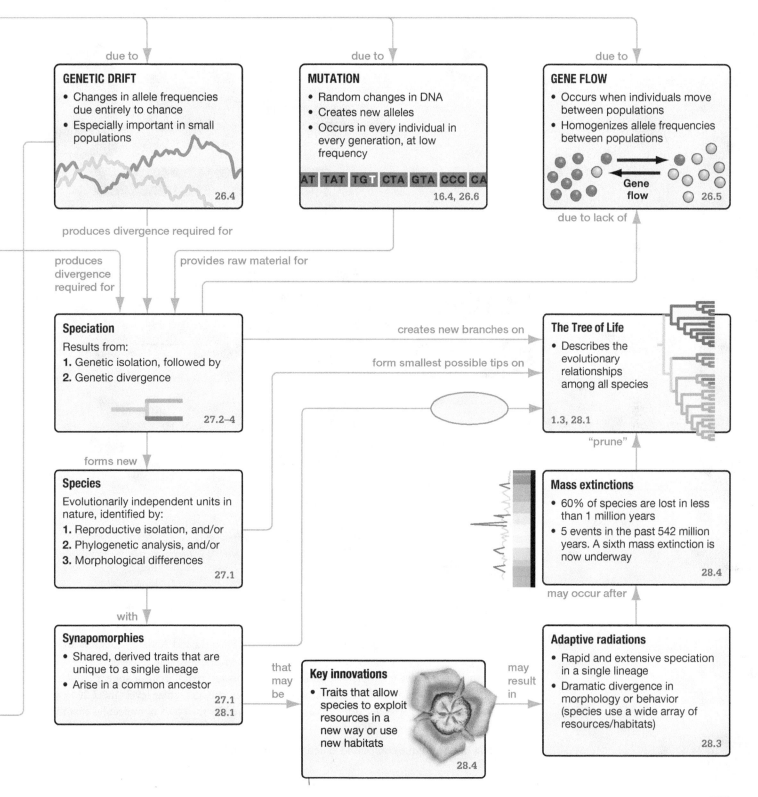

GENETIC DRIFT
- Changes in allele frequencies due entirely to chance
- Especially important in small populations

26.4

due to

MUTATION
- Random changes in DNA
- Creates new alleles
- Occurs in every individual in every generation, at low frequency

AT TAT TGT CTA GTA CCC CA

16.4, 26.6

due to

GENE FLOW
- Occurs when individuals move between populations
- Homogenizes allele frequencies between populations

Gene flow   26.5

due to lack of

produces divergence required for

produces divergence required for

provides raw material for

Speciation

Results from:
1. Genetic isolation, followed by
2. Genetic divergence

27.2–4

creates new branches on

form smallest possible tips on

The Tree of Life
- Describes the evolutionary relationships among all species

1.3, 28.1

"prune"

forms new

Species

Evolutionarily independent units in nature, identified by:
1. Reproductive isolation, and/or
2. Phylogenetic analysis, and/or
3. Morphological differences

27.1

Mass extinctions
- 60% of species are lost in less than 1 million years
- 5 events in the past 542 million years. A sixth mass extinction is now underway

28.4

may occur after

with

Synapomorphies
- Shared, derived traits that are unique to a single lineage
- Arise in a common ancestor

27.1
28.1

that may be

Key innovations
- Traits that allow species to exploit resources in a new way or use new habitats

28.4

may result in

Adaptive radiations
- Rapid and extensive speciation in a single lineage
- Dramatic divergence in morphology or behavior (species use a wide array of resources/habitats)

28.3

29 Bacteria and Archaea

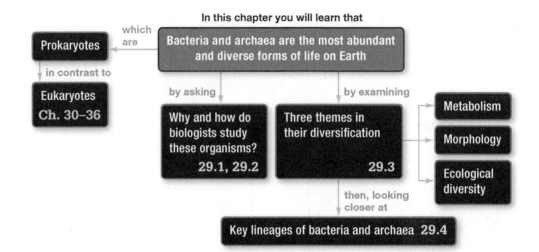

In this chapter you will learn that

Bacteria and archaea are the most abundant and diverse forms of life on Earth

which are → Prokaryotes

in contrast to → Eukaryotes Ch. 30–36

by asking → Why and how do biologists study these organisms? 29.1, 29.2

by examining → Three themes in their diversification 29.3 → Metabolism / Morphology / Ecological diversity

then, looking closer at → Key lineages of bacteria and archaea 29.4

Although this hot spring looks devoid of life, it is actually teeming with billions of bacterial and archaeal cells.

Bacteria and Archaea (usually pronounced *ar-KEE-ah*) form two of the three largest branches on the tree of life (**FIGURE 29.1**). The third major branch, or domain, consists of eukaryotes and is called the Eukarya. Virtually all members of the Bacteria and Archaea domains are unicellular, and all are prokaryotic—meaning that they lack a membrane-bound nucleus.

Although their relatively simple morphology makes bacteria and archaea appear similar to the untrained eye, in some ways they are strikingly different at the molecular level (**TABLE 29.1**). Organisms in the Bacteria and Archaea domains are distinguished by the types of molecules that make up their plasma membranes and cell walls:

- **Bacteria** have a unique compound called peptidoglycan in their cell walls (see Chapter 5).

✔ When you see this checkmark, stop and test yourself. Answers are available in Appendix A.

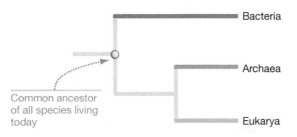

FIGURE 29.1 Bacteria, Archaea, and Eukarya Are the Three Domains of Life. Archaea are more closely related to eukaryotes than they are to bacteria.

✔**QUESTION** Was the common ancestor of all species living today prokaryotic or eukaryotic? Explain your reasoning.

- **Archaea** have unique phospholipids in their plasma membranes—the hydrocarbon tails of the phospholipids are made from isoprene (see Chapter 6).

If you were unicellular, bacteria and archaea would look as different to you as mammals and fish.

In addition, the machinery that bacteria and archaea use to process genetic information is strikingly different. More specifically, the DNA polymerases, RNA polymerases, transcription-initiation proteins, and ribosomes found in Archaea and Eukarya are distinct from those found in Bacteria and similar to each other. These differences have practical consequences: Antibiotics that poison bacterial ribosomes do not affect the ribosomes of archaea or eukaryotes. If all ribosomes were identical, these antibiotics would kill you along with the bacterial species that was supposed to be targeted.

As an introductory biology student, you may know less about bacteria and archaea than about any other group on the tree of life. Before taking this course, it's likely that you'd never even heard of the Archaea. You might be surprised to find out that biologists suspect that the first eukaryotic cells may have formed as a result of a symbiotic event between these two groups of prokaryotes. Notice in Table 29.1 that cells in the domain Eukarya share some features with both Bacteria and Archaea. Studying these shared features has helped biologists understand the early evolution of life on Earth.

This chapter's goal is to convince you that even though bacteria and archaea are tiny, they have an enormous impact on you and the planet in general. By the time you finish reading the chapter, you should understand why a researcher summed up the bacteria and archaea by claiming, "They run this joint."

29.1 Why Do Biologists Study Bacteria and Archaea?

Biologists study bacteria and archaea for the same reasons they study any organisms. First, they are intrinsically fascinating. Discoveries such as finding bacterial cells living a kilometer underground or in 95°C hot springs keep biologists awake at night, staring at the ceiling. They can't wait to get into the lab in the morning and figure out how those cells stay alive.

SUMMARY TABLE 29.1 **Characteristics of Bacteria, Archaea, and Eukarya**

	Bacteria	Archaea	Eukarya
DNA enclosed by a nuclear envelope? (see Chapter 7)	No	No	Yes
Circular chromosome present?	Yes (but linear in some species)	Yes	No (linear)
Organelles enclosed by membranes present? (see Chapter 7)	No	No	Yes
Rotating flagella present? (see Chapter 7)	Yes	Yes	No (flagella and cilia undulate)
Multicellular species?	No (with some exceptions)	No	Yes
Plasma membrane lipids composed of glycerol bonded to unbranched fatty acids by ester linkages? (see Chapter 6)	Yes	No (branched lipids bonded by ether linkages)	Yes
Cell walls, when present, contain peptidoglycan? (see Chapter 5)	Yes	No	No
RNA polymerase composed of >10 subunits?	No (only 5 subunits)	Yes	Yes
Translation initiated with methionine? (see Chapter 17)	No (initiated with N-formylmethionine; f-met)	Yes	Yes

✔**EXERCISE** Using the data in this table, add labeled marks to Figure 29.1 indicating where the following traits evolved: peptidoglycan in cell wall, archaeal-type plasma membrane, archaeal- and eukaryotic-type translation initiation, and nuclear envelope.

Second, there are practical benefits to understanding the species that share the planet with us. Understanding bacteria and archaea is particularly important—in terms of both understanding life on Earth and improving human health and welfare.

Biological Impact

The lineages in the domains Bacteria and Archaea are ancient, diverse, abundant, and ubiquitous. The oldest fossils of any type found to date are 3.5-billion-year-old carbon-rich deposits derived from bacteria. Because eukaryotes do not appear in the fossil record until 1.75 billion years ago, biologists infer that prokaryotes were the only form of life on Earth for at least 1.7 billion years.

Just how many bacteria and archaea are alive today? Although a mere 5000 species have been formally named and described to date, it is virtually certain that millions exist. Consider that over 1000 species of prokaryotes are living in your large intestine right now, and another 700 species are living in your mouth. Well-known microbiologist Norman Pace points out that there may be tens of millions of different insect species but notes, "If we squeeze out any one of these insects and examine its contents under the microscope, we find hundreds or thousands of distinct microbial species." Most of these **microbes** (microscopic organisms) are bacteria or archaea. Virtually all are unnamed and undescribed. If you want to discover and name new species, then study bacteria or archaea.

Abundance Besides recognizing how diverse bacteria and archaea are in terms of numbers of species, it's critical to appreciate their abundance.

- The approximately 10^{13} (10 trillion) cells in your body are outnumbered ten to one by the bacterial and archaeal cells living on and in you. You are a walking, talking habitat—one that is teeming with bacteria and archaea.

- A mere teaspoon of good-quality soil contains *billions* of microbial cells, most of which are bacteria and archaea.

- In sheer numbers, species in a lineage of marine archaea may be the most successful organisms on Earth. Biologists routinely find these cells at concentrations of over 10,000 individuals per milliliter in most of the world's oceans. At these concentrations, one liter of seawater contains a population equivalent to that of the largest human cities. Yet this lineage was not described until the early 1990s.

- Recent research has found enormous numbers of bacterial and especially archaeal cells in rocks and sediments as much as 1600 meters underneath the world's oceans. Although recently discovered, the bacteria and archaea living under the ocean may make up 10 percent of the world's total mass of living material.

- Biologists estimate the total number of individual bacteria and archaea alive today at over 5×10^{30}. If they were lined up end to end, these cells would make a chain longer than the Milky Way galaxy. They contain 50 percent of all the carbon and 90 percent of all the nitrogen and phosphorus found in organisms.

In terms of the total volume of living material on our planet, bacteria and archaea are dominant life-forms.

Habitat Diversity Bacteria and archaea are found almost everywhere. They live in environments as unusual as oxygen-free mud, hot springs, and salt flats. In seawater they are found from the surface to depths of 10,000 meters (m), and at temperatures over 120°C (well above water's boiling point) near submarine volcanoes.

Although there are far more prokaryotes than eukaryotes, much more is known about eukaryotic diversity than about prokaryotic diversity. Researchers who study prokaryotic diversity are exploring one of the most wide-open frontiers in all of science. So little is known about the extent of these domains that recent collecting expeditions have turned up entirely new **phyla** (singular: **phylum**). These are names given to major lineages within each domain. To a biologist, this achievement is equivalent to the sudden discovery of a new group of eukaryotes as distinctive as flowering plants or animals with backbones.

The physical world has been explored and mapped, and many of the larger plants and animals are named. But in **microbiology**—the study of organisms that can be seen only with the aid of a microscope—this is an age of exploration and discovery.

Some Microbes Thrive in Extreme Environments

Bacteria or archaea that live in high-salt, high-temperature, low-temperature, or high-pressure habitats are **extremophiles** ("extreme-lovers"). Studying them has been extraordinarily fruitful for understanding the tree of life, developing industrial applications, and exploring the structure and function of enzymes.

As an example of these habitats, consider hydrothermal vents at the bottom of the ocean, where water as hot as 300°C emerges and mixes with 4°C seawater. At locations like these, archaea are abundant forms of life.

Researchers recently discovered an archaeon that grows so close to these hydrothermal vents that its surroundings are at 121°C—a record for life at high temperature. This organism can live and grow in water that is heated past its boiling point (100°C) and at pressures that would instantly destroy a human. Since high temperature breaks non-covalent bonds holding macromolecules together, extreme heat usually denatures proteins, makes membranes leaky, and separates the strands of the DNA double helix. Biologists are intrigued by how these unusual archaeal cells can thrive under such extreme conditions.

Other discovered bacteria and archaea can grow

- at a pH less than 1.0;

- at temperatures of 0°C under Antarctic ice;

- in water that is virtually saturated with salt (**FIGURE 29.2**).

Extremophiles have become a hot area of research. The genomes of a wide array of extremophiles have been sequenced, and expeditions regularly seek to characterize new species. Why?

- *Origin of life* Based on models of conditions that prevailed early in Earth's history, it appears likely that the first forms of life lived at high temperature and pressure in environments

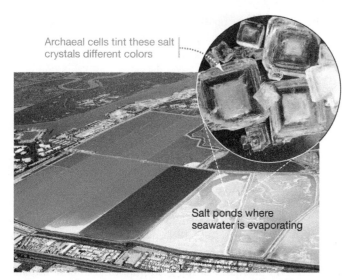

Archaeal cells tint these salt crystals different colors

Salt ponds where seawater is evaporating

FIGURE 29.2 Some Archaeal Cells Live in High-Salt Habitats. The evaporating water is colored red by these photosynthetic cells.

that lacked oxygen—conditions that humans would call extreme. Thus, understanding extremophiles may help explain how life on Earth began.

- *Extraterrestrial life?* In a similar vein, many astrobiologists ("space-biologists") use extremophiles as model organisms in the search for extraterrestrial life. The idea is that if bacteria and archaea can thrive in extreme habitats on Earth, cells might possibly be found in similar environments on other planets or moons of planets.

- *Commercial applications* Because enzymes that function at extreme temperatures and pressures are useful in many industrial processes, extremophiles are of commercial interest as well. Recall that *Taq* polymerase—a DNA polymerase that is stable up to 95°C—is used to run the polymerase chain reaction (PCR) in research and commercial settings (see Chapter 20). This enzyme was isolated from a bacterium called *Thermus aquaticus* ("hot water"), which was discovered in a hot spring in Yellowstone National Park.

Bacteria and archaea may be small, but they thrive in an amazing range of conditions.

Medical Importance

The first paper documenting that an archaeon was associated with a human disease—a dental condition called periodontitis—was published in 2004. But biologists have been studying disease-causing bacteria for over a century.

Of the thousands of bacterial species living in and on your body, only a tiny fraction can disrupt normal body functions enough to cause illness. Bacteria that cause disease are said to be **pathogenic** (literally, "disease-producing"). Pathogenic bacteria have been responsible for some of the most devastating epidemics in human history.

TABLE 29.2 lists some of the bacteria that cause illness in humans. Here are the important things to note:

- Pathogenic forms come from several different lineages in the domain Bacteria.

TABLE 29.2 **Some Bacteria That Cause Illness in Humans**

Lineage	Species	Tissues Affected	Disease
Firmicutes	*Clostridium tetani*	Wounds, nervous system	Tetanus
	Staphylococcus aureus	Skin, urogenital canal	Acne, boils, impetigo, toxic shock syndrome
	Streptococcus pneumoniae	Respiratory tract	Pneumonia
	Streptococcus pyogenes	Respiratory tract	Strep throat, scarlet fever
Spirochaetes	*Borrelia burgdorferi*	Skin and nerves	Lyme disease
	Treponema pallidum	Urogenital canal	Syphilis
Actinobacteria	*Mycobacterium tuberculosis*	Respiratory tract	Tuberculosis
	Mycobacterium leprae	Skin and nerves	Leprosy
	Propionibacterium acnes	Skin	Acne
Chlamydiales	*Chlamydia trachomatis*	Urogenital canal	Genital tract infection
ε-Proteobacteria	*Helicobacter pylori*	Stomach	Ulcer
β-Proteobacteria	*Neisseria gonorrhoeae*	Urogenital canal	Gonorrhea
γ-Proteobacteria	*Haemophilus influenzae*	Ear canal, nervous system	Ear infections, meningitis
	Pseudomonas aeruginosa	Urogenital canal, eyes, ear canal, lungs	Infections of eye, ear, urinary tract, lungs
	Salmonella enterica	Gastrointestinal tract	Food poisoning
	Yersinia pestis	Lymph and blood	Plague

- Pathogenic bacteria tend to affect tissues at the entry points to the body, such as wounds or pores in the skin, the respiratory and gastrointestinal tracts, and the urogenital canal.

Koch's Postulates Robert Koch was the first person to establish a link between a particular species of bacterium and a specific disease. When Koch began his work on the nature of disease in the late 1800s, microscopists had confirmed the existence of the particle-like organisms people now call bacteria, and Louis Pasteur had shown that bacteria and other microorganisms are responsible for spoiling milk, wine, broth, and other foods. Koch hypothesized that bacteria might also be responsible for causing infectious diseases, which spread by being passed from an infected individual to an uninfected individual.

Koch set out to test this hypothesis by identifying the organism that causes anthrax. Anthrax is a disease of cattle and other grazing mammals that can result in fatal blood poisoning. The disease also occurs infrequently in humans and mice.

To establish a causative link between a specific microbe and a specific disease, Koch proposed that four criteria had to be met:

1. The microbe must be present in individuals suffering from the disease and absent from healthy individuals. By careful microscopy, Koch was able to show that the bacterium *Bacillus anthracis* was always present in the blood of cattle suffering from anthrax, but absent from healthy individuals.

2. The organism must be isolated and grown in a pure culture away from the host organism. Koch was able to grow pure colonies of *B. anthracis* in glass dishes on a nutrient medium, using gelatin as a substrate.

3. If organisms from the pure culture are injected into a healthy experimental animal, the disease symptoms should appear. Koch demonstrated this crucial causative link in mice injected with *B. anthracis*. The symptoms of anthrax infection appeared and then the infected mice died.

4. The organism should be isolated from the diseased experimental animal, again grown in pure culture, and demonstrated by its size, shape, and color to be the same as the original organism. Koch did this by purifying *B. anthracis* from the blood of diseased experimental mice.

These criteria, now called **Koch's postulates,** are still used to confirm a causative link between new diseases and a suspected infectious agent. Microbiologists now recognize that many bacteria cannot be grown in culture, so they use other means of detection for those organisms.

The Germ Theory Koch's experimental results were the first test of the **germ theory of disease.**

- The pattern component of this theory is that certain diseases are infectious—meaning that they can be passed from person to person.
- The process responsible for this pattern is the transmission and growth of certain bacteria and viruses.

Viruses are acellular particles that parasitize cells (see Chapter 36).

The germ theory of disease laid the foundation for modern medicine. Initially its greatest impact was on sanitation—efforts to prevent transmission of pathogenic bacteria. During the American Civil War, for example, records indicate that more soldiers died of bacterial infections contracted from drinking water contaminated with human feces than from wounds in battle. Also during that conflict it was common for surgeons to sharpen their scalpels on their shoe leather, after walking in horse manure.

Fortunately, improvements in sanitation and nutrition have caused dramatic reductions in mortality rates due to infectious diseases in the industrialized countries.

What Makes Some Bacterial Cells Pathogenic? Virulence, or the ability to cause disease, is a heritable trait that varies among individuals in a population. Most *Escherichia coli*, for example, are harmless inhabitants of the gastrointestinal tract of humans and other mammals. But some *E. coli* cells cause potentially fatal food poisoning.

What makes some cells of the same species pathogenic, while others are harmless? Biologists have answered this question for *E. coli* by sequencing the entire genome of a harmless lab strain and the pathogenic strain called O157:H7, which is harmful to humans. The genome of the pathogenic strain is slightly larger because it has acquired virulence genes, including one coding for a protein **toxin.** After entering a host cell, this toxin binds to ribosomes and inhibits protein synthesis, killing the host cells. Because of key differences between the ribosomes of bacteria and eukaryotic cells, only host-cell protein synthesis is blocked by the toxin. Cells lining the blood vessels near the host's intestinal epithelium are most affected by the toxin, and the resulting damage leads to bloody diarrhea and possible death. If sanitation is poor, the pathogenic bacteria are likely to infect many new hosts.

Similar types of studies are identifying the genes responsible for virulence in a wide array of pathogenic bacteria.

The Past, Present, and Future of Antibiotics **Antibiotics** are molecules that kill bacteria or stop them from growing. They are produced naturally by a wide array of soil-dwelling bacteria and fungi. In these environments, antibiotics are hypothesized to help cells reduce competition for nutrients and other resources.

The discovery of antibiotics in 1928, their development over subsequent decades, and widespread use starting in the late 1940s gave physicians effective tools to combat many bacterial infections.

Unfortunately, extensive use of antibiotics in the late twentieth century in clinics and animal feed led to the evolution of drug-resistant strains of pathogenic bacteria (see Chapter 25). One study found that there are now soil-dwelling bacteria in natural environments that—far from being killed by antibiotics—actually use them as food.

Coping with antibiotic resistance in pathogenic bacteria has become a great challenge of modern medicine. Some researchers even claim that humans may be entering the "post-antibiotic era" in medicine.

New research indicates that bacteria have another advantage: They usually grow as **biofilms,** dense bacterial colonies enmeshed

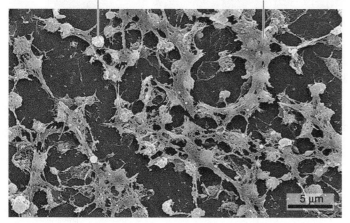

Bacterial cells (round)   Polysaccharide biofilm

5 µm

FIGURE 29.3 Biofilm Growing Inside a Catheter. This micrograph shows *Staphylococcus aureus* cells growing inside a catheter—a tube inserted into a body so that fluids can be withdrawn or injected. Bacterial communities that secrete polysaccharides and adhere to surfaces are sometimes more resistant to antibiotics.

FIGURE 29.4 Bacteria and Archaea Can Play a Role in Cleaning Up Pollution. These clean-up workers are spraying nitrogenous nutrients to encourage bacterial and archaeal growth following the 1989 *Exxon Valdez* oil spill in Alaska.

in a polysaccharide-rich matrix that helps shield the bacteria from antibiotics. Antibiotic-resistant biofilms on medical devices such as catheters are a growing problem in hospitals (**FIGURE 29.3**).

Role in Bioremediation

Bacteria are often in the news because of their dire medical effects. However, only a tiny proportion of bacteria and archaea actually cause disease in humans or other organisms. In the vast majority of cases, bacteria and archaea either have no direct impact on humans or are beneficial. For example, microbes play an important role in wastewater treatment efforts, and researchers are using bacteria and archaea to clean up sites polluted with organic solvents—an effort called **bioremediation.**

Throughout the industrialized world, some of the most serious pollutants in soils, rivers, and ponds consist of organic compounds that were originally used as solvents or fuels but leaked or were spilled into the environment. Most of these compounds are highly hydrophobic. Because they do not dissolve in water, they tend to accumulate in sediments. If the compounds are subsequently ingested by burrowing worms or clams or other organisms, they can be passed along to fish, insects, humans, birds, and other species.

At moderate to high concentrations, these pollutants are toxic to eukaryotes. Petroleum from oil spills and compounds that contain ring structures and chlorine atoms, such as the family of compounds called dioxins, are particularly notorious because of their toxicity to humans.

Fortunately, naturally existing populations of bacteria and archaea can grow in spills and degrade the toxins. This growth can be enhanced using two complementary bioremediation strategies:

1. *Fertilizing contaminated sites to encourage the growth of existing bacteria and archaea that degrade toxic compounds.* After several oil spills, researchers added nitrogen to affected sites as a fertilizer (**FIGURE 29.4**). Dramatic increases

occurred in the growth of bacteria and archaea that use hydrocarbons in cellular respiration, probably because the cells used the added nitrogen to synthesize enzymes and other key compounds. In at least some cases, the fertilized shorelines cleaned up much faster than unfertilized sites.

2. *"Seeding," or adding, specific species of bacteria and archaea to contaminated sites.* Seeding shows promise of alleviating pollution in some situations. For example, researchers have recently discovered bacteria that are able to render certain chlorinated, ring-containing compounds harmless. Instead of being poisoned by the pollutants, these bacteria use the chlorinated compounds as electron acceptors during cellular respiration. In at least some cases, the by-product is dechlorinated and nontoxic to humans and other eukaryotes.

To follow up on these discoveries, researchers are now growing the bacteria in quantity, to test the hypothesis that seeding can speed the rate of decomposition in contaminated sediments. Initial reports suggest that seeding may help clean up at least some polluted sites.

29.2 How Do Biologists Study Bacteria and Archaea?

Biologists' understanding of the domains Bacteria and Archaea is advancing more rapidly right now than at any time during the past 100 years—and perhaps faster than our understanding of any other lineages on the tree of life.

As an introduction to the domains Bacteria and Archaea, let's examine a few of the techniques that biologists use to answer questions about them. Some of these research strategies have been used since bacteria were first discovered; some were invented less than 10 years ago.

Using Enrichment Cultures

Which species of bacteria and archaea are present at a particular location, and what do they use as food? To answer questions like these, biologists rely heavily on their ability to culture organisms in the lab. Of the 5000 species of bacteria and archaea described to date, almost all were discovered when they were isolated from natural habitats and grown under controlled conditions in the laboratory.

One classical technique for isolating new types of bacteria and archaea is called **enrichment culture.** Enrichment cultures are based on establishing a specified set of growing conditions—temperature, lighting, substrate, types of available food, and so on. Cells that thrive under the specified conditions increase in numbers enough to be isolated and studied in detail.

To appreciate how this strategy works in practice, consider research on bacteria that live deep below Earth's surface. One study began with samples of rock and fluid from drilling operations in Virginia and Colorado. The samples came from sedimentary rocks at depths ranging from 860 to 2800 meters below the surface, where temperatures are between 42°C and 85°C. The questions posed in the study were simple: Is anything alive down there? If so, what do the organisms use to fuel cellular respiration?

The research team hypothesized that if organisms were living deep below the surface of the Earth, the cells might use hydrogen molecules (H_2) as an electron donor and the ferric ion (Fe^{3+}) as an electron acceptor (**FIGURE 29.5**). Recall that most eukaryotes use sugars as electron donors and use oxygen as an electron acceptor during cellular respiration (see Chapter 9). Fe^{3+} is the oxidized form of iron, and it is abundant in the rocks the biologists collected from great depths. It exists at great depths below the surface in the form of ferric oxyhydroxide, $Fe(OH)_3$. The researchers predicted that if an organism in the samples reduced the ferric ions during cellular respiration, then a black, oxidized, and magnetic mineral called magnetite (Fe_3O_4) would start appearing in the cultures as a by-product of cellular respiration.

What did their enrichment cultures produce? In some cultures, a black compound began to appear within a week. A variety of tests confirmed that the black substance was indeed magnetite. As the "Results" section of Figure 29.5 shows, microscopy revealed the organisms themselves—previously undiscovered bacteria. Because they grow only when incubated at 45°C–75°C, these organisms are considered **thermophiles** ("heat-lovers"). The discovery was spectacular—it was one of the first studies demonstrating that Earth's crust is teeming with organisms to depths of over a mile below the surface. Enrichment culture continues to be a productive way to isolate and characterize new species of bacteria and archaea.

Using Metagenomics

Researchers estimate that of all the bacteria and archaea living today, less than 1 percent have been grown in culture. To augment research based on enrichment cultures, researchers are

RESEARCH

QUESTION: Can bacteria live a mile below Earth's surface?

HYPOTHESIS: Bacteria are capable of cellular respiration deep below Earth's surface by using H_2 as an electron donor and Fe^{3+} as an electron acceptor.

NULL HYPOTHESIS: Bacteria from this environment are not capable of using H_2 as an electron donor and Fe^{3+} as an electron acceptor.

EXPERIMENTAL SETUP:

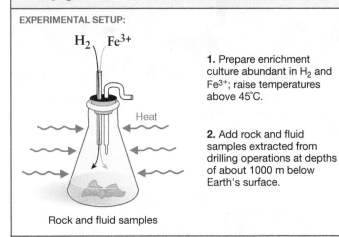

1. Prepare enrichment culture abundant in H_2 and Fe^{3+}; raise temperatures above 45°C.

2. Add rock and fluid samples extracted from drilling operations at depths of about 1000 m below Earth's surface.

PREDICTION: Black, magnetic grains of magnetite (Fe_3O_4) will accumulate because Fe^{3+} is reduced by growing cells and shed as a waste product. Cells will be visible.

PREDICTION OF NULL HYPOTHESIS: No magnetite will appear. No cells will grow.

RESULTS: Cells are visible, and magnetite is detectable.

CONCLUSION: At least one bacterial species that can live deep below Earth's surface grew in this enrichment culture. Different culture conditions might result in the enrichment of different species present in the same sample.

FIGURE 29.5 Enrichment Cultures Isolate Large Populations of Cells That Grow under Specific Conditions.

✔**QUESTION** Suppose no organisms had grown in this culture. Explain why the lack of growth would be either strong or weak evidence on the question of whether organisms live a mile below the Earth's surface.

SOURCE: Liu, S. V., J. Zhou, C. Zhang, et al. 1997. Thermophilic Fe(III)-reducing bacteria from the deep subsurface: the evolutionary implications. *Science* 277: 1106–1109.

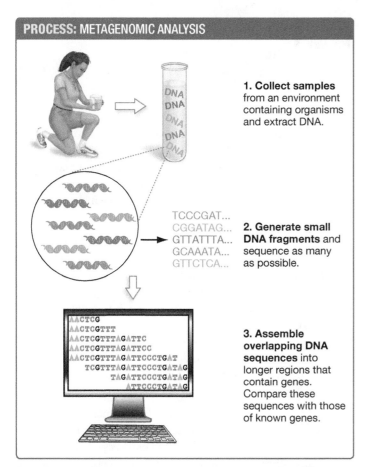

PROCESS: METAGENOMIC ANALYSIS

1. Collect samples from an environment containing organisms and extract DNA.

TCCCGAT...
CGGATAG...
GTTATTTA...
GCAAATA...
GTTCTCA...

2. Generate small DNA fragments and sequence as many as possible.

```
AACTCG
AACTCGTTT
AACTCGTTTAGATTC
AACTCGTTTAGATTCC
AACTCGTTTAGATTCCCTGAT
     TCGTTTAGATTCCCTGAT
         TAGATTCCCTGATAG
            ATTCCCTGATAG
```

3. Assemble overlapping DNA sequences into longer regions that contain genes. Compare these sequences with those of known genes.

FIGURE 29.6 Metagenomics Allows Researchers to Identify Species That Have Never Been Seen. Metagenomic analysis is used to generate DNA sequences from an environmental sample. That information can then be used to identify novel species and investigate biological processes.

employing a technique called **metagenomics** or **environmental sequencing** (see Chapter 21). Metagenomics is employed in part to document the presence of bacteria and archaea in an environmental sample that cannot be grown in culture. It is based on extracting and sequencing much of the DNA from a sample and then identifying species and biochemical pathways by comparing the DNA sequences with those of known genes. **FIGURE 29.6** outlines the steps performed in a metagenomics study.

Metagenomic analysis allows biologists to rapidly identify and characterize organisms that have never been seen. The technique has revealed huge new branches on the tree of life and produced revolutionary data on the habitats where bacteria and archaea are found.

In one recent study biologists extracted DNA from 125 human fecal samples and generated over 500 billion base pairs of sequence, over 150 times more than the entire human genome. The results they obtained are fascinating:

- In total, the samples contained about 1000 different species of bacteria. Some species were found in most of the samples while others were found in only a few of the humans sampled;

- the vast majority of bacterial species identified were from three phyla: Bacteroidetes, Firmicutes, and Actinobacteria;

- the identified bacterial genes that were shared by all of the human subjects suggest that bacteria play important roles in human physiology, including digestion of complex carbohydrates and synthesis of essential amino acids and vitamins.

Results like these make it clear that humans harbor a diverse ecosystem of symbiotic bacteria. Some bacteria may make us sick, but we depend on many others to stay healthy.

In combination with **direct sequencing**—a technique based on isolating and sequencing a specific gene from organisms found in a particular habitat—metagenomics is revolutionizing biologists' understanding of bacterial and archaeal diversity.

Evaluating Molecular Phylogenies

To put data from enrichment culture and metagenomic studies into context, biologists depend on the accurate placement of species on phylogenetic trees. Recall that phylogenetic trees illustrate the evolutionary relationships among species and lineages (see Chapter 1, Chapter 28, and **BioSkills 7** in Appendix B). They are a pictorial summary of which species are more closely or distantly related to others.

Some of the most useful phylogenetic trees for the Bacteria and the Archaea have been based on studies of the RNA molecules found in the small subunit of ribosomes, or what biologists call 16S and 18S RNA. (See Chapter 17 for more information on the structure and function of ribosomes.) In the late 1960s Carl Woese and colleagues began a massive effort to determine and compare the base sequences of 16S and 18S RNA molecules from a wide array of species. The result of their analysis was the **tree of life**, illustrated in Figure 29.1.

check your understanding

C Y U

If you understand that . . .

- Enrichment cultures isolate cells that grow in response to specific conditions. They create an abundant sample of bacteria that thrive under particular conditions, allowing further study.
- Metagenomics is based on isolating DNA from samples taken directly from the environment, generating random DNA fragments for sequencing, and then analyzing the DNA sequences to identify the organisms and genes present.

✔ **You should be able to . . .**

1. Design an enrichment culture that would isolate species that could be used to clean up oil spills.

2. Outline a study designed to identify the bacterial and archaeal species present in a soil sample near the biology building on your campus.

Answers are available in Appendix A.

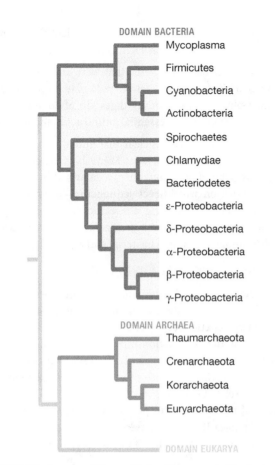

DOMAIN BACTERIA
- Mycoplasma
- Firmicutes
- Cyanobacteria
- Actinobacteria
- Spirochaetes
- Chlamydiae
- Bacteriodetes
- ε-Proteobacteria
- δ-Proteobacteria
- α-Proteobacteria
- β-Proteobacteria
- γ-Proteobacteria

DOMAIN ARCHAEA
- Thaumarchaeota
- Crenarchaeota
- Korarchaeota
- Euryarchaeota

DOMAIN EUKARYA

FIGURE 29.7 Phylogeny of Some Major Lineages in Bacteria and Archaea.

Woese's tree is now considered a classic result. Before its publication, biologists thought that the major division among organisms was between prokaryotes and eukaryotes. But based on data from ribosomal RNA molecules, the major divisions of life-forms are actually the Bacteria, Archaea, and Eukarya. Tracing the early evolutionary history of these domains is extremely difficult since the events distinguishing the lineages took place so long ago. In addition, lateral gene transfer (described in Chapter 21) has blurred the boundaries of the domains. However, recent studies suggest that Eukarya may have formed from a symbiosis between an archaeal cell and a bacterial cell. Traits of both lineages are found within Eukarya (see Chapter 30).

More recent analyses of morphological and molecular characteristics have succeeded in identifying a large series of monophyletic groups within the domains. Recall that a **monophyletic group** consists of an ancestral population and all of its descendants (see Chapter 28). Monophyletic groups can also be called clades or lineages.

The phylogenetic tree in **FIGURE 29.7** summarizes recent results but is still considered highly provisional. Work on molecular phylogenies continues at a brisk pace. Section 29.4 explores some of these lineages in detail, but for now let's turn to the question of how all this diversification took place.

29.3 What Themes Occur in the Diversification of Bacteria and Archaea?

At first, the diversity of bacteria and archaea can seem almost overwhelming. To make sense of the variation among lineages and species, biologists focus on two themes in diversification: morphology and metabolism. Regarding metabolism, the key question is which molecules are used as food. Bacteria and archaea are capable of living in a wide array of environments because they vary in cell structure and in how they make a living.

Morphological Diversity

Because we humans are so large, it is hard for us to appreciate the morphological diversity that exists among bacteria and archaea. To us, they all look small and similar. But at the scale of a bacterium or archaean, different species are wildly diverse in morphology.

Size, Shape, and Motility   To appreciate how diverse these organisms are in terms of morphology, consider bacteria alone:

- *Size*   Bacterial cells range in size from the smallest of all free-living cells—bacteria called mycoplasmas with volumes as small as 0.15 μm^3—to the largest bacterium known, *Thiomargarita namibiensis*, which has volumes as large as $200 \times 10^6 \ \mu m^3$. Over a billion *Mycoplasma* cells could fit inside an individual *T. namibiensis* (**FIGURE 29.8a**).

- *Shape*   Bacterial cells range in shape from filaments, spheres, rods, and chains to spirals (**FIGURE 29.8b**).

- *Motility*   Many bacterial cells are motile; their swimming movements are powered by rotating flagella. Depending on the direction of rotation, cells either swim ahead or tumble, which allows them to change direction. Gliding movement, which enables cells to creep along a surface, also occurs in several groups, though the molecular mechanism responsible for this form of motility is still unknown (**FIGURE 29.8c**).

Cell-Wall Composition   For single-celled organisms, the composition of the plasma membrane and cell wall are particularly important. The introduction to this chapter highlights the dramatic differences between the plasma membranes and cell walls of bacteria versus archaea.

Within bacteria having cell walls, biologists distinguish two general types of wall using a dyeing system called the **Gram stain.** As **FIGURE 29.9a** shows, Gram-positive cells look purple but Gram-negative cells look pink.

At the molecular level, most cells that are **Gram-positive** have a plasma membrane surrounded by a cell wall with extensive peptidoglycan (**FIGURE 29.9b**). You might recall that peptidoglycan is a complex substance composed of carbohydrate strands that are cross-linked by short chains of amino acids (see Chapter 5). Most cells that are **Gram-negative,** in contrast, have a plasma

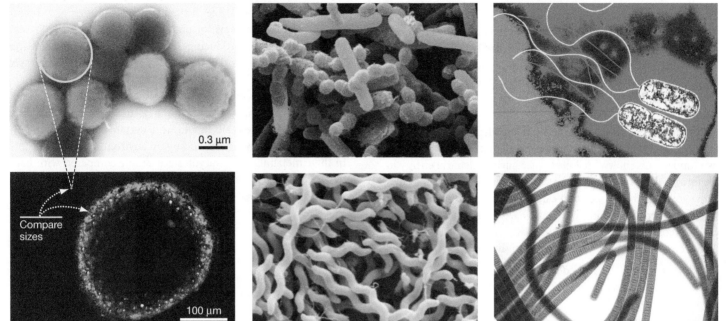

(a) Size varies.

Most bacteria are about 1 μm in diameter, but some are much larger.

Smallest (*Mycoplasma mycoides*)

0.3 μm

Compare sizes

Largest (*Thiomargarita namibiensis*)

100 μm

(b) Shape varies...

... from rods to spheres to spirals. In some species, cells adhere to form chains.

Rods, chains of spheres (compost bacteria)

Spirals (*Campylobacter jejuni*)

(c) Motility varies.

Some bacteria are nonmotile, but swimming and gliding are common.

Swimming (*Pseudomonas aeruginosa*)

Gliding (*Oscillatoria limosa*)

FIGURE 29.8 Morphological Diversity among Bacteria Is Extensive. Some of the cells in these micrographs have been colorized to make them more visible.

membrane surrounded by a cell wall that has two components—a thin gelatinous layer containing peptidoglycan and an outer phospholipid bilayer (**FIGURE 29.9c**).

Analyzing cell cultures with the Gram stain can be an important preliminary step in treating bacterial infections. Because they contain so much peptidoglycan, Gram-positive cells may respond to treatment by penicillin-like drugs that disrupt peptidoglycan synthesis. Gram-negative cells, in contrast, are more

likely to be affected by erythromycin or other types of drugs that poison bacterial ribosomes.

To summarize, members of the Bacteria and the Archaea are remarkably diverse in their overall size, shape, and motility as well as in the composition of their cell walls and plasma membranes. But when asked to name the innovations that were most responsible for the diversification of these two domains, biologists do not point to their morphological diversity. Instead, they

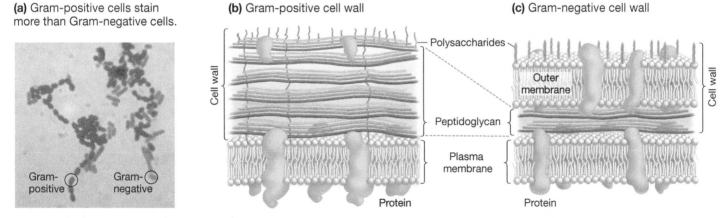

(a) Gram-positive cells stain more than Gram-negative cells.

Gram-positive   Gram-negative

(b) Gram-positive cell wall

Cell wall

Polysaccharides

Peptidoglycan

Plasma membrane

Protein

(c) Gram-negative cell wall

Outer membrane

Peptidoglycan

Cell wall

Protein

FIGURE 29.9 Gram Staining Distinguishes Two Types of Cell Walls in Bacteria. Cells with extensive peptidoglycan retain a large amount of stain and look purple; others retain little stain and look pink, as can be seen in part (a).

point to metabolic diversity—variation in the chemical reactions that go on inside these cells.

Metabolic Diversity

The most important thing to remember about bacteria and archaea is how diverse they are in the types of compounds they can use as food. Bacteria and archaea are the masters of metabolism. Taken together, they can subsist on almost anything—from hydrogen molecules to crude oil. Bacteria and archaea look small and relatively simple to us in their morphology, but their biochemical capabilities are dazzling.

Just how varied are bacteria and archaea when it comes to making a living? To appreciate the answer, recall that all organisms have two fundamental nutritional needs—acquiring chemical energy in the form of adenosine triphosphate (ATP) and obtaining molecules with carbon–carbon bonds that can be used as building blocks for the synthesis of fatty acids, proteins, DNA, RNA, and other large, complex compounds required by the cell.

Bacteria and archaea produce ATP in three ways:

1. **Phototrophs** ("light-feeders") use light energy to excite electrons. ATP is produced by photophosphorylation (see Chapter 10).

2. **Chemoorganotrophs** oxidize organic molecules with high potential energy, such as sugars. ATP may be produced by cellular respiration—with sugars serving as electron donors—or via fermentation pathways (see Chapter 9).

3. **Chemolithotrophs** ("rock-feeders") oxidize inorganic molecules with high potential energy, such as ammonia (NH_3) or methane (CH_4). ATP is produced by cellular respiration, and inorganic compounds serve as the electron donor.

Bacteria and archaea fulfill their second nutritional need—obtaining building-block compounds with carbon–carbon bonds—in two ways:

1. By synthesizing their own compounds from simple starting materials such as CO_2 and CH_4. Organisms that manufacture their own building-block compounds are termed **autotrophs** ("self-feeders").

2. By absorbing ready-to-use organic compounds from their environment. Organisms that acquire building-block compounds from other organisms are called **heterotrophs** ("other-feeders").

Because there are three distinct ways of producing ATP and two general mechanisms for obtaining carbon, there are a total of six methods for producing ATP and obtaining carbon. The names that biologists use for organisms that employ these six "feeding strategies" are given in **TABLE 29.3**.

Of the six possible ways of producing ATP and obtaining carbon, just two are observed among eukaryotes. But bacteria and archaea do them all. In addition, certain species can switch among modes of living, depending on environmental conditions. In their metabolism, eukaryotes are simple compared with bacteria and archaea. ✔ If you understand the essence of metabolic diversity in bacteria and archaea, you should be able to match the six example species described in **TABLE 29.4** to the appropriate category in Table 29.3.

What makes this remarkable diversity possible? Bacteria and archaea have evolved dozens of variations on the basic processes of respiration and photosynthesis (see Chapters 9 and 10). They use compounds with high potential energy to produce ATP via cellular respiration (electron transport chains) or fermentation, they use light to produce high-energy electrons, and they reduce carbon from CO_2 or other sources to produce sugars or other building-block molecules with carbon–carbon bonds.

The story of bacteria and archaea can be boiled down to two sentences: The basic chemistry required for photosynthesis, cellular respiration, and fermentation originated in these lineages. Then the evolution of variations on each of these processes allowed prokaryotes to diversify into millions of species that occupy diverse habitats. Let's take a closer look.

Producing ATP Through Cellular Respiration: Variation in Electron Donors and Acceptors Millions of bacterial, archaeal, and eukaryotic species—including animals and some plants—are chemoorganotrophs. These organisms obtain the energy required to make ATP by breaking down organic compounds such as sugars, starch, or fatty acids.

SUMMARY TABLE 29.3 **Six General Methods for Obtaining Energy and Carbon–Carbon Bonds**

		Source of C–C Bonds (for synthesis of complex organic compounds)	
		Autotrophs: self-synthesized from CO_2, CH_4, or other simple molecules	**Hetero**trophs: from molecules produced by other organisms
Source of Energy (for synthesis of ATP)	**Photo**trophs: from sunlight	photoautotrophs	photoheterotrophs
	Chemoorganotrophs: from organic molecules	chemoorganoautotrophs	chemoorganoheterotrophs
	Chemolithotrophs: from inorganic molecules	chemolitho[auto]trophs	chemolithotrophic heterotrophs

TABLE 29.4 Six Examples of Metabolic Diversity

Example	How ATP Is Produced	How Building-Block Molecules Are Synthesized
Cyanobacteria	via oxygenic photosynthesis	from CO_2 via the Calvin cycle
Clostridium aceticum	via fermentation of glucose	from CO_2 via reactions called the acetyl-CoA pathway
Ammonia-oxidizing archaea (e.g., *Nitrosopumilus* sp.)	via cellular respiration, using ammonia (NH_3) as an electron donor	from CO_2 via the Calvin cycle
Helicobacteria	via anoxygenic photosynthesis	absorb carbon-containing building-block molecules from the environment
Escherichia coli	via fermentation of organic compounds or cellular respiration, using organic compounds as electron donors	absorb carbon-containing building-block molecules from the environment
Beggiatoa	via cellular respiration, using hydrogen sulfide (H_2S) as an electron donor	absorb carbon-containing building-block molecules from the environment

Cellular enzymes can strip electrons from organic molecules that have high potential energy and then transfer these high-energy electrons to the electron carriers NADH and $FADH_2$ (see Chapter 9). These compounds feed electrons to an electron transport chain (ETC), where electrons are stepped down from a high-energy state to a low-energy state (**FIGURE 29.10a**). In eukaryotic cells the ETC is located in the highly folded inner mitochondrial membrane. In bacteria and archaea, this membrane is the plasma membrane.

The energy that is released allows components of the ETC to generate a proton gradient across the plasma membrane (**FIGURE 29.10b**). The resulting flow of protons back through the enzyme ATP synthase results in the production of ATP, via the process called chemiosmosis.

The essence of this process, called **cellular respiration,** is that a molecule with high potential energy serves as an original electron donor and is oxidized, while a molecule with low potential energy serves as a final electron acceptor and becomes reduced. The potential energy difference between the electron donor and electron acceptor is eventually transformed into chemical energy in the form of ATP or is used for other processes (see Chapter 9).

(a) Model of Electron Transport Chain (ETC)

(b) ETC generates proton gradient across plasma membrane.

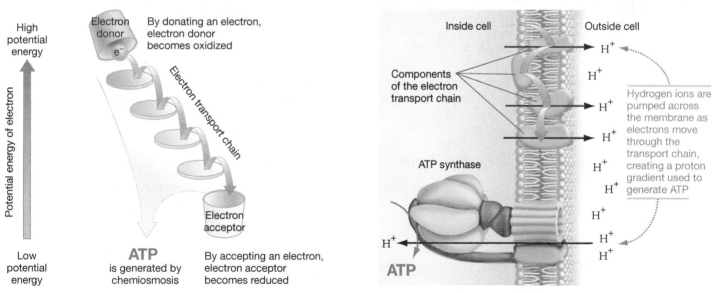

FIGURE 29.10 Cellular Respiration Is Based on Electron Transport Chains. Protons may diffuse away from the cell but a gradient will still form.

✔**EXERCISE** In part (a), add the chemical formula for a specific electron donor, electron acceptor, and reduced by-product for a species of bacteria or archaea. Then write in the electron donor, electron acceptor, and reduced by-product observed in humans.

Most eukaryotes carry out aerobic respiration:

- Organic compounds with high potential energy—often glucose—serve as the original electron donor. When cellular respiration is complete, glucose is completely oxidized to CO_2, which is given off as a by-product.

- Oxygen is the final electron acceptor, and water is also produced as a by-product.

Many bacteria and archaea also rely on these molecules.

It is common, however, to find bacteria and archaea that employ an electron donor other than sugars and an electron acceptor other than oxygen during cellular respiration. These species produce by-products other than carbon dioxide and water (TABLE 29.5):

- Molecules with high potential energy serve as electron donors. The substances used as electron donors range from hydrogen molecules (H_2) and hydrogen sulfide (H_2S) to ammonia (NH_3) and methane (CH_4).

- Compounds with relatively low potential energy—including sulfate (SO_4^{2-}), nitrate (NO_3^-), carbon dioxide (CO_2), or ferric ions (Fe^{3+})—act as electron acceptors.

It is only a slight exaggeration to claim that researchers have found bacterial and archaeal species that can use almost any compound with relatively high potential energy as an electron donor and almost any compound with relatively low potential energy as an electron acceptor.

Because the electron donors and electron acceptors used by bacteria and archaea are so diverse, one of the first questions biologists ask about a species is whether it undergoes cellular respiration—and if so, how. The best way to answer this question is through the enrichment culture technique introduced in Section 29.2. Recall that in an enrichment culture, researchers supply specific electron donors and electron acceptors in the medium and try to isolate cells that can use those compounds to support growth.

The remarkable metabolic diversity of bacteria and archaea explains why they play such a key role in cleaning up some types of pollution. Species that use organic solvents or petroleum-based fuels as electron donors or electron acceptors may excrete waste products that are less toxic than the original compounds.

Producing ATP via Fermentation: Variation in Substrates One strategy for making ATP that does not involve electron transport chains is called **fermentation** (see Chapter 9). In fermentation, no outside electron acceptor is used.

Because fermentation is a much less efficient way to make ATP compared with cellular respiration, in many species it occurs as an alternative metabolic strategy when no electron acceptors are available to make cellular respiration possible. In other species, fermentation does not occur at all. But in many bacteria and archaea, fermentation is the only way that cells make ATP.

Although some eukaryotic organisms can ferment glucose to ethanol or lactic acid (see Chapter 9), some bacteria and archaea are capable of using other organic compounds as the starting point for fermentation. Bacteria and archaea that produce ATP via fermentation are still classified as organotrophs, but they are much more diverse in the substrates used. For example:

- The bacterium *Clostridium aceticum* can ferment ethanol, acetate, and fatty acids as well as glucose.

- Other species of *Clostridium* ferment complex carbohydrates (including cellulose or starch), proteins, purines, or amino acids. Species that ferment amino acids produce by-products with names such as cadaverine and putrescine. These molecules are responsible for the odor of rotting flesh.

- Other bacteria can ferment lactose, a prominent component of milk. In some species this fermentation has two end products: propionic acid and CO_2. Propionic acid is responsible for the taste of Swiss cheese; the CO_2 produced during fermentation creates the holes in cheese.

- Many bacterial species in the human digestive tract ferment complex carbohydrates in our diet. The human cells then absorb the by-products and extract even more energy from them using O_2 as the final electron acceptor.

The diversity of enzymatic pathways observed in bacterial and archaeal fermentations extends the metabolic repertoire of these organisms. The diversity of substrates that are fermented also

TABLE 29.5 **Some Electron Donors and Acceptors Used by Bacteria and Archaea**

Electron Donor	By-Product from Electron Donor	Electron Acceptor	By-Product from Electron Acceptor	Category*
Sugars	CO_2	O_2	H_2O	Organotrophs
H_2 or organic compounds	H_2O or CO	SO_4^{2-}	H_2S or S^{2-}	Sulfate reducers
H_2	H_2O	CO_2	CH_4	Methanogens
CH_4	CO_2	O_2	H_2O	Methanotrophs
H_2S or S^{2-}	SO_4^{2-}	O_2	H_2O	Sulfur bacteria
Organic compounds	CO_2	Fe^{3+}	Fe^{2+}	Iron reducers
NH_3	NO_2^-	O_2	H_2O	Ammonia oxidizers
Organic compounds	CO_2	NO_3^-	N_2O, NO, or N_2	Nitrate reducers

*The name biologists use to identify species that use a particular metabolic strategy.

supports the claim that as a group, bacteria and archaea can use virtually any molecule with relatively high potential energy as a source of high-energy electrons for producing ATP.

Producing ATP via Photosynthesis: Variation in Electron Sources and Pigments

Instead of using molecules as a source of high-energy electrons, phototrophs pursue a radically different strategy: **photosynthesis.** Among bacteria and archaea, photosynthesis can happen in three different ways:

1. Light activates a pigment called bacteriorhodopsin, which uses the absorbed energy to transport protons across the plasma membrane and out of the cell. The resulting flow of protons back into the cell drives the synthesis of ATP via chemiosmosis (see Chapter 9).

2. A recently discovered bacterium that lives near hydrothermal vents on the ocean floor performs photosynthesis not by absorbing light, but by absorbing geothermal radiation.

3. Pigments that absorb light raise electrons to high-energy states. As these electrons are stepped down to lower energy states by electron transport chains, the energy released is used to generate ATP.

An important feature of this last mode of photosynthesis is that the process requires a source of electrons (see Chapter 10). Recall that in cyanobacteria and plants, the required electrons come from water. When these organisms "split" water molecules apart to obtain electrons, they generate oxygen as a by-product. Species that use water as a source of electrons for photosynthesis are said to complete **oxygenic** ("oxygen-producing") photosynthesis.

In contrast, many phototrophic bacteria use a molecule other than water as the source of electrons. In some cases, the electron donor is hydrogen sulfide (H_2S); a few species can use the ion known as ferrous iron (Fe^{2+}). Instead of producing oxygen as a by-product of photosynthesis, these cells produce elemental sulfur (S) or the ferric ion (Fe^{3+}). This type of photosynthesis is said to be **anoxygenic** ("no oxygen-producing").

The photosynthetic pigments found in plants are chlorophylls *a* and *b* (see Chapter 10). Cyanobacteria have these two pigments. But researchers have isolated seven additional chlorophylls from different lineages of bacterial phototrophs. Each lineage has one or more of these distinctive chlorophylls, and each type of chlorophyll absorbs light best at a different wavelength. ✔ If you understand that different photosynthetic bacteria contain different kinds of light-absorbing pigments, you should be able to explain how several different photosynthetic species can live in the same habitat without competing for light.

Obtaining Building-Block Compounds: Variation in Pathways for Fixing Carbon

In addition to acquiring energy, organisms must obtain building-block molecules that contain carbon–carbon bonds. Organisms use two mechanisms to procure usable carbon—either making their own or getting it from other organisms (see Chapters 9 and 10). Autotrophs make their own building-block compounds; heterotrophs consume them.

In many autotrophs, including cyanobacteria and plants, the enzymes of the Calvin cycle transform carbon dioxide (CO_2) into organic molecules that can be used in synthesizing cell material. The carbon atom in CO_2 is reduced during the process and is said to be "fixed." Animals and fungi, in contrast, obtain carbon from living plants or animals, or by absorbing the organic compounds released as dead tissues decay.

Bacteria and archaea pursue these same two strategies. Some interesting twists occur among bacterial and archaeal autotrophs, however. Not all of them use the Calvin cycle to make building-block molecules, and not all start with CO_2 as a source of carbon atoms. For example, consider these biochemical pathways:

- Some proteobacteria are called **methanotrophs** ("methane-eaters") because they use methane (CH_4) as their carbon source. (They also use CH_4 as an electron donor in cellular respiration.) Methanotrophs process CH_4 into more complex organic compounds via one of two enzymatic pathways, depending on the species.

- Some bacteria can use carbon monoxide (CO) or methanol (CH_3OH) as a starting material.

These observations drive home an important message from this chapter: Compared with eukaryotes, the metabolic capabilities of bacteria and archaea are remarkably complex and diverse.

Ecological Diversity and Global Impacts

The metabolic diversity observed among bacteria and archaea explains why these organisms can thrive in such a wide array of habitats.

- The array of electron donors, electron acceptors, and fermentation substrates exploited by bacteria and archaea allows the heterotrophic species to live just about anywhere.

- The evolution of three distinct types of photosynthesis—based on bacteriorhodopsin, geothermal energy, or pigments that donate high-energy electrons to ETCs—extends the types of habitats that can support phototrophs.

The complex chemistry that these cells carry out, combined with their numerical abundance, has made them potent forces for global change throughout Earth's history. Bacteria and archaea have altered the chemical composition of the oceans, atmosphere, and terrestrial environments for billions of years. They continue to do so today.

The Oxygen Revolution

Today, oxygen represents almost 21 percent of the molecules in Earth's atmosphere. But researchers who study the composition of the atmosphere are virtually certain that no free molecular oxygen (O_2) existed for the first 2.3 billion years of Earth's existence. This conclusion is based on two observations:

1. There was no plausible source of oxygen at the time the planet formed.

2. Chemical analysis of the oldest Earth rocks suggests that they formed in the absence of atmospheric oxygen.

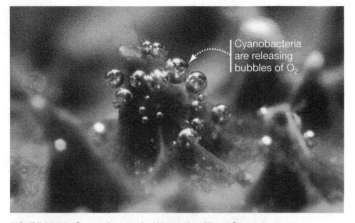

FIGURE 29.11 Cyanobacteria Were the First Organisms to Perform Oxygenic Photosynthesis.

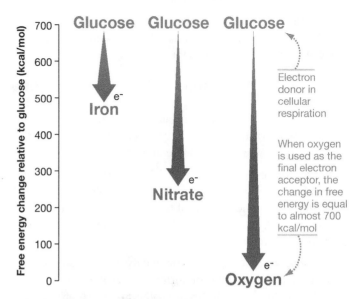

FIGURE 29.12 Cellular Respiration Can Produce More Energy When Oxygen Is the Final Electron Acceptor. More potential energy in glucose can be released when oxygen is the final acceptor compared to other molecules or ions.

DATA: Wilson, D. F., M. Erecińska, and P. L. Dutton. 1974. *Annual Review of Biophysics and Bioengineering 3*: 203–230; Tables 1 and 3.

✔**QUESTION** Which organisms grow faster—those using aerobic respiration or those using anaerobic respiration? Explain your reasoning.

Early in Earth's history, the atmosphere was dominated by nitrogen and carbon dioxide. Where did the oxygen we breathe come from? The answer is cyanobacteria.

Cyanobacteria is a lineage of photosynthetic bacteria. According to the fossil record, species of cyanobacteria first became numerous in the oceans about 2.7–2.5 billion years ago. Their appearance was momentous because cyanobacteria were the first organisms to perform oxygenic ("oxygen-producing") photosynthesis (**FIGURE 29.11**).

The fossil record and geologic record indicate that oxygen concentrations in the oceans and atmosphere began to increase 2.3–2.1 billion years ago. Once oxygen was common in the oceans, cells could begin to use it as the final electron acceptor during cellular respiration. **Aerobic** respiration was now a possibility. Before that, organisms had to use compounds other than oxygen as a final electron acceptor—only **anaerobic** respiration was possible. (Aerobic and anaerobic respiration are introduced in Chapter 9.)

The evolution of aerobic respiration was a crucial event in the history of life. Because oxygen is extremely electronegative, it is an efficient electron acceptor. Much more energy is released as electrons move through electron transport chains with oxygen as the ultimate acceptor than is released with other substances as the electron acceptor.

To drive this point home, study the graph in **FIGURE 29.12**. Notice that the vertical axis plots free energy changes; the graph shows the energy released when glucose is oxidized with iron, nitrate, or oxygen as the final electron acceptor. Once oxygen was available, then, cells could produce much more ATP for each electron donated by NADH or $FADH_2$. As a result, the rate of energy production rose dramatically.

To summarize, data indicate that cyanobacteria were responsible for a fundamental change in Earth's atmosphere—a high concentration of oxygen. Never before, or since, have organisms done so much to alter the nature of our planet.

Nitrogen Fixation and the Nitrogen Cycle

In many environments, fertilizing forests or grasslands with nitrogen results in increased growth. Researchers infer from these results that plant growth is often limited by the availability of nitrogen.

Organisms must have nitrogen to synthesize proteins and nucleic acids. Although molecular nitrogen (N_2) is extremely abundant in the atmosphere, most organisms cannot use it because of the strong triple bond linking the nitrogen atoms. To incorporate nitrogen atoms into amino acids and nucleotides, all eukaryotes and many bacteria and archaea have to obtain N in a form such as ammonia (NH_3) or nitrate (NO_3^-).

Certain bacteria and archaea are the only species that are capable of converting molecular nitrogen to ammonia. The steps in the process, called **nitrogen fixation,** are highly endergonic reduction-oxidation (redox) reactions (see Chapter 9). The key enzyme that catalyzes the reaction—nitrogenase—is found only in selected bacterial and archaeal lineages. Many of these organisms are free living, but some form important relationships with plants:

- Some species of cyanobacteria live in association with a water fern that grows in rice paddies and helps fertilize the plants.

- In terrestrial environments, nitrogen-fixing bacteria live in close association with plants—often taking up residence in special root structures called nodules (see Chapter 39).

Why is nitrogenase not found in all organisms? The answer lies in an interesting property of the enzyme. When exposed to O_2, nitrogenase is irreversibly poisoned and is degraded. The only organisms with the nitrogenase gene are those that live in anaerobic habitats or are able to protect the enzyme from O_2.

Nitrogen fixation is only the beginning of the story, however. A quick glance back at Table 29.5 should convince you that bacteria and archaea use a wide array of nitrogen-containing

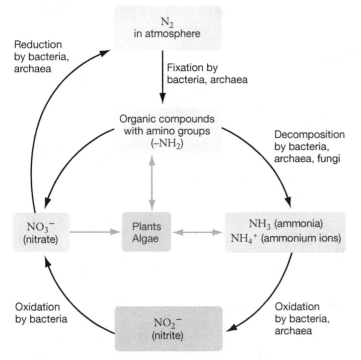

FIGURE 29.13 **Bacteria and Archaea Drive the Movement of Nitrogen Atoms through Ecosystems.** Nitrogen atoms cycle in different molecular forms.

✔EXERCISE Add arrows and labels to indicate that animals ingest amino groups from plants or other animals and release amino groups or ammonia.

compounds as electron donors and electron acceptors during cellular respiration.

To understand why this is important, consider that the nitrite (NO_2^-) produced by some bacteria as a by-product of respiration does not build up in the environment. Instead, other species of bacteria and archaea use it as an electron donor, and it is oxidized to molecular nitrate (NO_3^-). Nitrate, in turn, is reduced to molecular nitrogen (N_2) by yet another suite of bacterial and archaeal species. In this way, bacteria and archaea are responsible for driving the movement of nitrogen atoms through ecosystems around the globe in a process called the **nitrogen cycle** (**FIGURE 29.13**).

Similar types of interactions occur with molecules that contain phosphorus, sulfur, and carbon. In this way, bacteria and archaea play a key role in the cycling of nitrogen and other nutrients. ✔ If you understand the role of bacteria and archaea in the nitrogen cycle, you should be able to provide a plausible explanation of what the composition of the atmosphere and what the nitrogen cycle might be like if bacteria and archaea did not exist.

Nitrate Pollution Most crop plants—including corn, rice, and wheat—do not live in association with nitrogen-fixing bacteria. To increase yields of these crops, farmers use fertilizers that are high in nitrogen. In parts of the world, massive additions of nitrogen in the form of ammonia are causing serious pollution problems.

FIGURE 29.14 shows why. When ammonia is added to a cornfield—in midwestern North America, for example—much of

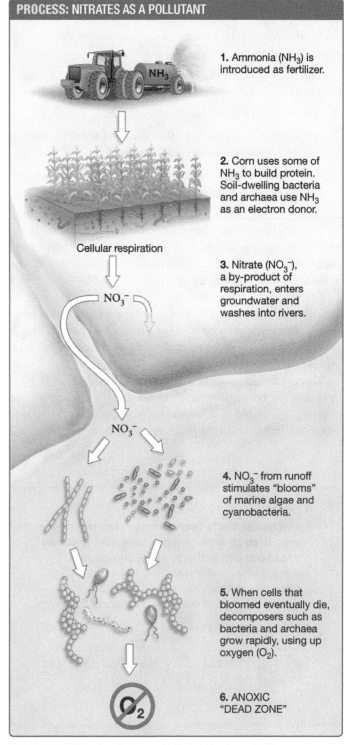

FIGURE 29.14 **Nitrates Act as a Pollutant in Aquatic Ecosystems.**

it never reaches the growing corn plants. Instead, bacteria and archaea in the soil use a significant fraction of the ammonia as food. Microbes that use ammonia as an electron donor to fuel cellular respiration release nitrite (NO_2^-) as a waste product. Other microbes use nitrite as an electron donor and release nitrate (NO_3^-). Nitrate molecules are extremely soluble in water and tend to be washed out of soils into groundwater or streams.

From there they eventually reach the ocean, where they can cause pollution.

To understand why nitrates can pollute the oceans, consider the Gulf of Mexico:

1. Nitrates carried by the Mississippi River are used as a nutrient by cyanobacteria and algae that live in the Gulf.

2. These cells explode in numbers in response.

3. When they die and sink to the bottom of the Gulf, bacteria and archaea and other decomposers use them as food.

4. The decomposers use so much oxygen as an electron acceptor in cellular respiration that oxygen levels in the sediments and even in Gulf waters decline.

Nitrate pollution has been so severe that large areas in the Gulf of Mexico are anoxic (lacking in oxygen). The oxygen-free "dead zone" in the Gulf of Mexico is devoid of fish, shrimp, and other organisms that require oxygen.

Lately, the dead zone has encompassed about 22,000 square kilometers (km^2)—roughly the size of New Jersey. Similar problem spots are cropping up in other parts of the world. Virtually every link in the chain of events leading to nitrate pollution involves bacteria and archaea.

The general message of this section is simple: Bacteria and Archaea may be small in size, but because of their abundance, ubiquity, and ability to do sophisticated chemistry, they have an enormous influence on the global environment.

check your understanding

If you understand that . . .

C Y U

- As a group, Bacteria and Archaea can use a wide array of electron donors and acceptors in cellular respiration and a diverse set of compounds in fermentation, perform anoxygenic as well as oxygenic photosynthesis, and fix carbon from several different sources via a variety of pathways.

✔ **You should be able to . . .**

Defend the claim that the metabolism of bacteria and archaea is much more sophisticated than that of eukaryotes.

Answers are available in Appendix A.

29.4 Key Lineages of Bacteria and Archaea

In the decades since the phylogenetic tree identifying the three domains of life was first published, dozens of studies have confirmed the result. It is now well established that all organisms alive today belong to one of the three domains, and that archaea and eukaryotes are more closely related to each other than either group is to bacteria.

Although the relationships among the major lineages within Bacteria and Archaea are still uncertain in some cases, many of the lineages themselves are well studied. Let's survey the attributes of species from selected major lineages within the Bacteria and Archaea, with an emphasis on themes explored earlier in the chapter: their morphological and metabolic diversity, their impacts on humans, and their importance to other species and to the environment.

Bacteria

The name *bacteria* comes from the Greek root *bacter*, meaning "rod" or "staff." The name was inspired by the first bacteria to be seen under a microscope, which were rod shaped. But as the following descriptions indicate, bacterial cells come in a wide variety of shapes.

Biologists who study bacterial diversity currently recognize at least 21 lineages, or phyla, within the domain. Some of these lineages were recognized by distinctive morphological characteristics and others by phylogenetic analyses of gene sequence data. The lineages reviewed here are just a sampling of bacterial diversity.

- Bacteria > Firmicutes
- Bacteria > Cyanobacteria
- Bacteria > Actinobacteria
- Bacteria > Spirochaetes (Spirochetes)
- Bacteria > Chlamydiae
- Bacteria > Proteobacteria

Archaea

The name *archaea* comes from the Greek root *archae*, for "ancient." The name was inspired by the hypothesis that this is a particularly ancient group, which turned out to be incorrect. Also incorrect was the initial hypothesis that archaeans are restricted to hot springs, salt ponds, and other extreme habitats. Archaea live in virtually every habitat known.

Recent phylogenies based on DNA sequence data indicate that the domain is composed of at least four major phyla, called the Thaumarchaeota, Crenarchaeota, Euryarchaeota, and Korarchaeota. The Korarchaeota are known only from direct sequencing studies. They have never been grown in culture, and almost nothing is known about them.

- Archaea > Thaumarchaeota
- Archaea > Crenarchaeota
- Archaea > Euryarchaeota

The Firmicutes have also been called "low-GC Gram positives" because their cell walls react positively to the Gram stain and because their DNA contains a relatively low percentage of guanine and cytosine (G and C). In some species, G and C represent less than 25 percent of the bases present. There are over 1100 species. ✔ You should be able to mark the origin of the Gram-positive cell wall on Figure 29.7.

Morphological diversity Most are rod shaped or spherical. Some of the spherical species form chains or tetrads (groups of four cells). A few form a durable resting stage called a spore. One subgroup synthesizes a cell wall made of cellulose.

Metabolic diversity Some species can fix nitrogen; some perform anoxygenic photosynthesis. Others make all of their ATP via various fermentation pathways; still others perform cellular respiration, using hydrogen gas (H_2) as an electron donor.

Human and ecological impacts Recent metagenomic studies have shown that members of this lineage are extremely common in the human gut. Species in this group also cause a variety of diseases, including anthrax, botulism, tetanus, walking pneumonia, boils, gangrene, and strep throat. *Bacillus thuringiensis* produces a toxin that is one of the most important insecticides currently used in farming. Species in the lactic acid bacteria group are used to ferment milk products into yogurt or cheese (**FIGURE 29.15**).

Lactobacillus bulgaricus (rods) and *Streptococcus thermophilus*

FIGURE 29.15 Firmicutes in Yogurt. (The cells in this scanning electron micrograph have been colorized.)

The cyanobacteria were formerly known as the "blue-green algae"—even though algae are eukaryotes. Only about 80 species of cyanobacteria have been described to date, but they are among the most abundant organisms on Earth. In terms of total mass, cyanobacteria dominate the surface waters in many marine and freshwater environments.

Morphological diversity Cyanobacteria may be found as independent cells, in chains that form filaments (**FIGURE 29.16**), or in the loose aggregations of individual cells called colonies. The shape of *Nostoc* colonies varies from flat sheets to ball-like clusters of cells.

Metabolic diversity All perform oxygenic photosynthesis; many can also fix nitrogen. Because cyanobacteria can synthesize virtually every molecule they need, they can be grown in culture media that contain only CO_2, N_2, H_2O, and a few mineral nutrients. Some species associate with fungi, forming lichens, while others form associations with protists, sponges, or plants. In each case the cyanobacterium provides some form of nutritional benefit to the host. ✔ You should be able to mark the origin of oxygenic photosynthesis on Figure 29.7.

Human and ecological impacts If cyanobacteria are present in high numbers, their waste products can make drinking water smell bad. Some species release molecules called microcystins that are toxic to plants and animals. Cyanobacteria were responsible for the origin of the oxygen atmosphere on Earth. Today they still produce much of the oxygen and nitrogen and many of the organic compounds that feed other organisms in freshwater and marine environments.

Nostoc species

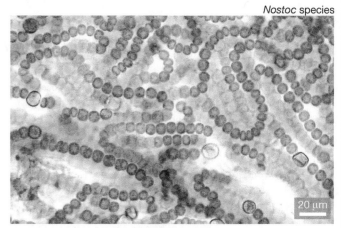

FIGURE 29.16 Cyanobacteria Contain Chlorophyll and Are Green.

Actinobacteria are sometimes called the "high-GC Gram positives" because (1) their cell-wall material appears purple when treated with the Gram stain—meaning that they have a peptidoglycan-rich cell wall and lack an outer membrane—and (2) their DNA contains a relatively high percentage of guanine and cytosine. In some species, G and C represent over 75 percent of the bases present. Over 1100 species have been described to date (**FIGURE 29.17**). ✔ You should be able to mark the origin of this high-GC genome on Figure 29.7.

Morphological diversity Cell shape varies from rods to filaments. Many of the soil-dwelling species are found as chains of cells that form extensive branching filaments called **mycelia.** Because of their morphology they were initially misclassified as fungi, and the incorrect name Actinomyces persists.

Metabolic diversity Many are heterotrophs that use an array of organic compounds as electron donors and oxygen as an electron acceptor. There are several parasitic species that get most of their nutrition from host organisms.

Human and ecological impacts Two serious human diseases, tuberculosis and leprosy, are caused by parasitic *Mycobacterium* species. Over 500 distinct antibiotics have been isolated from species in the genus *Streptomyces*; 60 of these—including streptomycin, neomycin, tetracycline, and erythromycin—are now actively prescribed to treat diseases in humans or domestic livestock. One actinobacterium species is critical to the manufacture of Swiss cheese. Species in the genus *Streptomyces* and *Arthrobacter* are abundant in soil and are vital as decomposers of dead plant and animal material. Some species live in association with plant roots and fix nitrogen; others can break down toxins such as herbicides, nicotine, and caffeine.

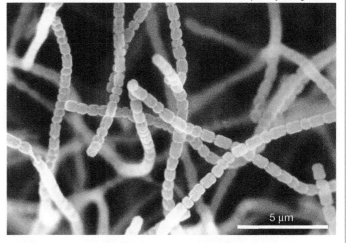

Streptomyces griseus

5 μm

FIGURE 29.17 A *Streptomyces* Species That Produces the Antibiotic Streptomycin.

Based on numbers of species, the spirochetes are one of the smaller bacterial phyla: Only 13 genera and a total of 62 species have been described to date.

Morphological diversity Spirochetes are distinguished by their unique corkscrew shape and flagella (**FIGURE 29.18**). Instead of extending into the water surrounding the cell, spirochete flagella are contained within a structure called the outer sheath, which surrounds the cell. When these flagella beat, the cell lashes back and forth and swims forward. ✔ You should be able to mark the origin of the spirochete flagellum on Figure 29.7.

Metabolic diversity Most spirochetes manufacture ATP via fermentation. The substrate used in fermentation varies among species and may consist of sugars, amino acids, starch, or the pectin found in plant cell walls. A spirochete that lives only in the hindgut of termites can fix nitrogen.

Human and ecological impacts The sexually transmitted disease syphilis is caused by a spirochete. Syphilis is thought to have been brought by European explorers to the Western hemisphere, where it was responsible for killing tens of millions of native people. Lyme disease, also caused by a spirochete, is transmitted to humans by deer ticks. Spirochetes are extremely common in freshwater and marine habitats; many live only under anaerobic conditions.

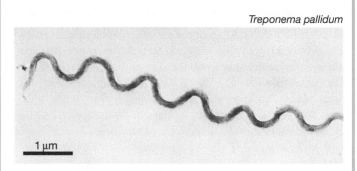

Treponema pallidum

1 μm

FIGURE 29.18 Spirochetes Are Corkscrew-Shaped Cells Inside an Outer Sheath.

In terms of numbers of species living today, Chlamydiae may be the smallest of all major bacterial lineages. Although the group is highly distinct phylogenetically, only 13 species are known. All are Gram-negative.

Morphological diversity Chlamydiae are spherical. They are tiny, even by bacterial standards.

Metabolic diversity All known species in this phylum live as parasites *inside* host cells and are termed **endosymbionts** ("inside-together-living"). Chlamydiae acquire almost all of their nutrition from their hosts. In **FIGURE 29.19**, the chlamydiae have been colored red; the animal cells that they live in are colored brown. ✔ You should be able to mark the origin of the endosymbiotic lifestyle in this lineage on Figure 29.7. (The endosymbiotic lifestyle has also arisen in other bacterial lineages, independently of Chlamydiae.)

Human and ecological impacts *Chlamydia trachomatis* infections are the most common cause of blindness in humans. When the same organism is transmitted from person to person via sexual intercourse, it can cause serious urogenital tract infections. If untreated in women, this disease can lead to ectopic pregnancy, premature births, and infertility. One species causes epidemics of a pneumonia-like disease in birds.

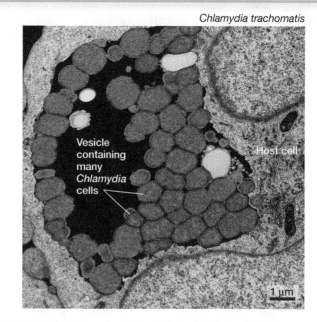

Chlamydia trachomatis

Vesicle containing many *Chlamydia* cells

Host cell

1 μm

FIGURE 29.19 Chlamydiae Live Only Inside Animal Cells.

The approximately 1200 species of proteobacteria form five major subgroups, designated by the Greek letters α (alpha), β (beta), γ (gamma), δ (delta), and ε (epsilon). Because they are so diverse in their morphology and metabolism, the lineage is named after the Greek god Proteus, who could assume many shapes.

Morphological diversity Proteobacterial cells can be rods, spheres, or spirals. Some form stalks (**FIGURE 29.20a**). Some are motile. In one group, cells may move together to form colonies, which then transform into the specialized cell aggregate shown in **FIGURE 29.20b**. This structure is known as a **fruiting body.** At their tips, the fruiting bodies produce cells that are surrounded by a durable coating. These spores sit until conditions improve, and then they resume growth.

Metabolic diversity Proteobacteria make a living in virtually every way known to bacteria—except that none perform oxygenic photosynthesis. Various species may perform cellular respiration by using organic compounds, nitrite, methane, hydrogen gas, sulfur, or ammonia as electron donors and oxygen, sulfate, or sulfur as electron acceptors. Some perform anoxygenic photosynthesis.

Human and ecological impacts *Escherichia coli* may be the best studied of all organisms and is a key species in biotechnology (see Chapter 20, and **BioSkills 13** in Appendix B). Pathogenic proteobacteria cause Legionnaire's disease, cholera, food poisoning, plague, dysentery, gonorrhea, Rocky Mountain spotted fever, typhus, ulcers, and diarrhea. *Wolbachia* infections are common in insects and are often transmitted from mothers to offspring

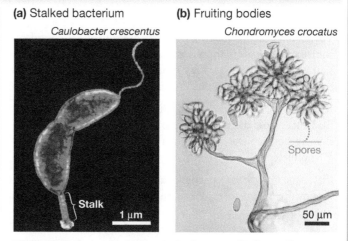

(a) Stalked bacterium
Caulobacter crescentus

Stalk

1 μm

(b) Fruiting bodies
Chondromyces crocatus

Spores

50 μm

FIGURE 29.20 Some Proteobacteria Grow on Stalks or Form Fruiting Bodies. The stalked bacterium (a) has been colorized.

via eggs. Biologists use *Agrobacterium* cells to transfer new genes into crop plants. Certain acid-loving species of proteobacteria are used in the production of vinegars. Species in the genus *Rhizobium* (α-proteobacteria) live in association with plant roots and fix nitrogen. A group in the δ-proteobacteria, the bdellovibrios, are predators—they drill into other proteobacterial cells and digest them. Because some species use nitrogen-containing compounds as electron acceptors, proteobacteria are critical players in the cycling of nitrogen atoms through terrestrial and aquatic ecosystems.

The Thaumarchaeota were recently recognized as a monophyletic, ancient lineage of archaea. Members of this phylum are extremely abundant in oceans, estuaries, and terrestrial soils. Unlike the extremophiles, species in this lineage are considered mesophilic because they grow best at moderate temperatures.

Morphological diversity Only a few members of this group have been observed, and all consist of rod-shaped cells that are less than 1 micrometer (μm) in length, smaller than typical prokaryotes. One species, *Nitrosopumilus maritimus* (**FIGURE 29.21**), is so abundant it is estimated to constitute possibly 25 percent of the total prokaryotic cell biomass in open oceans.

Metabolic diversity Members of this phylum are called ammonia oxidizers because they use ammonia as a source of electrons and generate nitrite as a by-product. They use the energy from ammonia oxidation to fix CO_2.

Human and ecological impacts Because of their abundance, these organisms are thought to play a major role in Earth's nitrogen and carbon cycles (see Chapter 56). Their presence in deep ocean waters that lack reduced carbon and sunlight may help explain the productivity of these habitats. The species *Cenarchaeum symbiosum* lives as an endosymbiont inside a marine sponge.

Nitrosopumilus maritimus

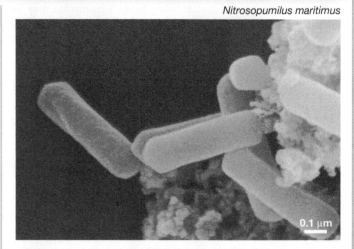

0.1 μm

FIGURE 29.21 This Species of Thaumarchaeota Has Rod-Shaped Cells and Is Extremely Abundant in the Open Ocean.

✔**QUANTITATIVE** Use the scale bar in the figure to measure the length of a *N. maritimus* cell. If these cells were placed end to end, how many of them would fit along a meter stick?

The Crenarchaeota got their name because they are considered similar to the oldest archaeans; the word root *cren–* refers to a source or fount. Biologists have named only 37 species so far, but they are virtually certain that thousands are yet to be discovered.

Morphological diversity Crenarchaeota cells can be shaped like filaments, rods, discs, or spheres. One species that lives in extremely hot habitats has a tough cell wall consisting solely of glycoprotein.

Metabolic diversity Depending on the species, cellular respiration can involve organic compounds, sulfur, hydrogen gas, or Fe^{2+} ions as electron donors and oxygen, nitrate, sulfate, sulfur, carbon dioxide, or Fe^{3+} ions as electron acceptors. Some species make ATP exclusively through fermentation pathways.

Human and ecological impacts Crenarchaeota have yet to be used in the manufacture of commercial products. In certain extremely hot, high-pressure, cold, or acidic environments, crenarchaeota may be the only life-form present (**FIGURE 29.22**). Acid-loving species thrive in habitats with pH 1–5; some species are found in ocean sediments at depths ranging from 2500 to 4000 m below the surface.

Sulfolobus species

0.5 μm

FIGURE 29.22 Some Crenarchaeota Live in Sulfur-Rich Hot Springs. The cells in the micrograph have been colorized to make them more visible.

The Euryarchaeota are aptly named, because the word root *eury*– means "broad." Members of this phylum live in every conceivable habitat. Some species are adapted to high-salt habitats with pH 11.5—almost as basic as household ammonia. Other species are adapted to acidic conditions with a pH as low as 0. Species in the genus *Methanopyrus* live near hot springs called black smokers that are 2000 m (over 1 mile) below sea level (**FIGURE 29.23**).

Morphological diversity Euryarchaeota cells can be spherical, filamentous, rod shaped, disc shaped, or spiral. Rod-shaped cells may be short or long or arranged in chains. Spherical cells can be found in ball-like aggregations. Some species have several flagella. Some species lack a cell wall; others have a cell wall composed entirely of glycoproteins.

Metabolic diversity The group includes a variety of methane-producing species. These **methanogens** can use up to 11 different organic compounds as electron acceptors during cellular respiration; all produce CH_4 as a by-product of respiration. In other species of Euryarchaeota, cellular respiration is based on hydrogen gas or Fe^{2+} ions as electron donors and nitrate or sulfate as electron acceptors. Species that live in high-salt environments can use the molecule retinal—which is responsible for light reception in your eyes—to capture light energy and perform photosynthesis.

Human and ecological impacts Species in the genus *Ferroplasma* live in piles of waste rock near abandoned mines. As a by-product of metabolism, they produce acids that drain into streams and pollute them. Methanogens live in the soils of swamps and the guts of mammals (including yours). They are responsible for adding about 2 billion tons of methane to the atmosphere each year. A methanogen in this phylum was also recently implicated in gum disease.

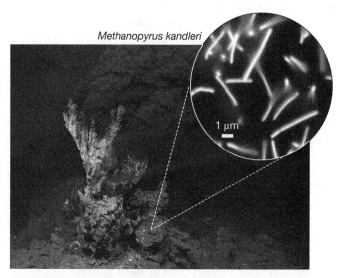

Methanopyrus kandleri

1 μm

FIGURE 29.23 Some Euryarchaeota Cells Live in the Chimneys of "Black Smokers" on the Seafloor.

CHAPTER 29   REVIEW

For media, go to MasteringBiology (MB)

If you understand . . .

29.1 Why Do Biologists Study Bacteria and Archaea?

- Bacteria and archaea are the most abundant organisms on Earth and are found in every habitat that has been sampled.

- Bacteria and archaea are very small, prokaryotic cells, and most are unicellular.

- Bacteria and archaea can be distinguished by their different kinds of membrane lipids and cell walls as well as by their different transcription machinery.

- Bacteria play many beneficial roles in animal digestion, bioremediation, and the production of antibiotics.

- Bacteria cause some of the most dangerous human diseases, including plague, syphilis, botulism, cholera, and tuberculosis.

✔ You should be able to explain the difference between a bacterium, an archaeon, and a eukaryote.

29.2 How Do Biologists Study Bacteria and Archaea?

- Enrichment cultures are used to grow large numbers of bacterial or archaeal cells that thrive under specified conditions.

- Using metagenomic analysis, biologists can study bacteria and archaea that cannot be cultured by extracting DNA directly from an environment and then sequencing and characterizing DNA fragments. Information obtained is used to identify biochemical processes and novel organisms that are then placed on the tree of life.

✔ You should be able to explain how metagenomic analysis might be used to reveal whether bacteria carry out nitrogen fixation in the gut of an insect.

29.3 What Themes Occur in the Diversification of Bacteria and Archaea?

- Metabolic diversity and complexity are the hallmarks of the bacteria and archaea, just as morphological diversity and complexity are the hallmarks of the eukaryotes.

- Among bacteria and archaea, a wide array of inorganic or organic compounds with high potential energy may serve as electron donors in cellular respiration, and a wide variety of inorganic or organic molecules with low potential energy may serve as electron acceptors. Dozens of distinct organic compounds are fermented.

- Photosynthesis is widespread in bacteria. In cyanobacteria, water is used as a source of electrons and oxygen gas is generated as a by-product. But in other species, the electron excited by photon capture comes from a source other than water, and no oxygen is produced.

- To acquire building-block molecules containing carbon–carbon bonds, some bacteria and archaea species use the enzymes of the Calvin cycle to reduce CO_2. But several other biochemical pathways found in bacteria and archaea can also reduce simple organic compounds to sugars or carbohydrates.

- Because of their metabolic diversity, bacteria and archaea play a large role in carbon and nitrogen cycling and alter the global atmosphere, oceans, and terrestrial environments.

- Nitrogen-fixing species provide nitrogen in forms that can be used by many other species, including plants and animals.

✔ You should be able to explain why species that release H_2S as a by-product and that use H_2S as an electron donor often live side by side.

29.4 Key Lineages of Bacteria and Archaea

- Prokaryotes can be divided into two lineages, the Bacteria and the Archaea, based on a wide variety of morphological, biochemical, and molecular characters.

- Bacteria are divided into 21 major lineages including organisms that play major roles in ecosystems as primary producers, decomposers, and parasites.

- Archaea are divided into four major lineages and were thought to exist only in extreme environments; they are now recognized to be widespread.

(MB) **MasteringBiology**

1. **MasteringBiology Assignments**

   Tutorials and Activities Classification of Prokaryotes, Diversity in Bacteria, Tree of Life, Water Pollution from Nitrates

   Questions Reading Quizzes, Blue-Thread Questions, Test Bank

2. **eText** Read your book online, search, take notes, highlight text, and more.

3. **The Study Area** Practice Test, Cumulative Test, BioFlix® 3-D Animations, Videos, Activities, Audio Glossary, Word Study Tools, Art

You should be able to . . .

✔ **TEST YOUR KNOWLEDGE**   *Answers are available in Appendix A*

1. How do the molecules that function as electron donors and those that function as electron acceptors differ?
   a. Electron donors are almost always organic molecules; electron acceptors are always inorganic.
   b. Electron donors are almost always inorganic molecules; electron acceptors are always organic.
   c. Electron donors have relatively high potential energy; electron acceptors have relatively low potential energy.
   d. Electron donors have relatively low potential energy; electron acceptors have relatively high potential energy.

2. What do some photosynthetic bacteria use as a source of electrons instead of water?
   a. oxygen (O_2)
   b. hydrogen sulfide (H_2S)
   c. organic compounds (e.g., CH_3COO^-)
   d. nitrate (NO_3^-)

3. What is distinctive about the chlorophylls found in different photosynthetic bacteria?
   a. their membranes
   b. their role in acquiring energy
   c. their role in carbon fixation
   d. their absorption spectra

4. What are organisms called that use inorganic compounds as electron donors in cellular respiration?
   a. phototrophs
   b. heterotrophs
   c. organotrophs
   d. lithotrophs

5. True or False. Certain aerobic bacteria in the presence of oxygen can convert nitrogen gas to ammonia.

6. Unlike plant cell walls that contain cellulose, bacterial cell walls are composed of _____.

7. What has metagenomic analysis allowed researchers to do for the first time?
   a. sample organisms from an environment and grow them under defined conditions in the lab
   b. isolate organisms from an environment and sequence their entire genome
   c. study organisms that cannot be cultured (grown in the lab)
   d. identify important morphological differences among species

8. Biologists often use the term energy source as a synonym for "electron donor." Why?

9. The text claims that the tremendous ecological diversity of bacteria and archaea is possible because of their impressive metabolic diversity. Do you agree with this statement? Why or why not?

10. Would you predict that disease-causing bacteria, such as those listed in Table 29.2, obtain energy from light, organic molecules, or inorganic molecules? Explain your answer.

11. The text claims that the evolution of an oxygen atmosphere paved the way for increasingly efficient cellular respiration and higher growth rates in organisms. Explain.

12. From what we know about the evolutionary relationship between the three largest domains, as depicted in Figure 29.1, explain the statement, "Prokaryotes are a paraphyletic group."

13. When using Koch's postulates, which of the following is an essential requirement for the suspected pathogen?
    a. It is present in all organisms with the disease.
    b. It can be cultured on an agar plate.
    c. It is pathogenic on a wide variety of organisms.
    d. It can reproduce sexually within the host.

14. The researchers who observed that magnetite was produced by bacterial cultures from the deep subsurface carried out a follow-up experiment. These biologists treated some of the cultures with a drug that poisons the enzymes involved in electron transport chains. In cultures where the drug was present, no more magnetite was produced. Does this result support or undermine their hypothesis that the bacteria in the cultures perform cellular respiration? Explain your reasoning.

15. *Streptococcus mutans* obtains energy by oxidizing sucrose. This bacterium is abundant in the mouths of Western European and North American children and is a prominent cause of cavities. The organism is virtually absent in children from East Africa, where tooth decay is rare. Propose a hypothesis to explain this observation. Outline the design of a study that would test your hypothesis.

16. Suppose that you've been hired by a firm interested in using bacteria to clean up organic solvents found in toxic waste dumps. Your new employer is particularly interested in finding cells that are capable of breaking a molecule called benzene into less toxic compounds. Where would you go to look for bacteria that can metabolize benzene as an energy or carbon source? How would you design an enrichment culture capable of isolating benzene-metabolizing species?

Credits

Photo Credits